The First Official
WINDOW DECORATING GUIDE
By Marie Graber

CONTENTS

7

DEDICATION

This book is dedicated to the millions of homemakers
throughout the world and to the opportunity
for decorating fun given them by their windows. It is
also dedicated to the thousands of interior
designers and retailers who offer them trained
assistance whenever they need it.

Hello there:

Thank you for your interest in my FIRST OFFICIAL WINDOW DECORATING GUIDE. In this book, organized for easy reference, you will find new ideas for each room in your home together with the how-to-do-it and required drapery fixture information. I hope you will find it helpful.

Decorating or "dressing" your windows can be fun. It certainly can be rewarding. Often the proper selection of treatment and associated drapery fixtures can change or amplify the entire mood or personality of a room. It's not unlike the artist's final brush stroke that makes the picture complete and meaningful.

I believe that windows are truly the most important consideration in home decorating. Here is the one element that not only sets a focal point inside your home, but is also a thing of beauty for the outside world. You might say that we see through our windows and that the world sees us through them, too.

Today's homemaker has all the necessary qualifications to become a near-professional decorator, even without formal training. All that is needed is to couple an existing sense of what is attractive with specific practical information. This is what my book is designed to do. Here are "idea starters" with which you can do exciting things that will make your neighbors wonder at your skill.

To make your job easier, today's manufacturers of drapery fixtures provide products that reflect the latest trends, performance advantages and conveniences and styling to meet the constantly changing decorating needs of the homemaker. Then, of course, the ultimate success of your window decorating efforts depends not only upon the treatment you pursue but also the fabrics and colors you choose to employ.

For on-the-spot help with any window decorating problem and for specific advice on color and fabric, there is no substitute for your dealer or an interior designer. But should you run into a problem so unique that even they cannot solve it, do not hesitate to write to me at Middleton, Wisconsin and I will do my very best to help.

9

Cordially yours,

Marie Graber

Marie Graber

ACKNOWLEDGMENTS

The author wishes to acknowledge the valued assistance and counsel of the many people who have contributed in many different ways to this publication of THE FIRST OFFICIAL WINDOW DECORATING GUIDE.

First of all, we recognize the hundreds of interior designers in private practice and in department stores who are a consistent source of new ideas such as those used in the GUIDE. This group, too numerous to mention individually, ranges from Bangkok to New York to Paris. We thank them with the most sincere hope that they continue to grow both in numbers and in stature.

Then there are the people at The Singer Company who contributed to the section on sewing draperies.

And no note of recognition could be complete without a special acknowledgment to my brother, Joseph V. Graber, President of The Graber Company, and the many fine Graber employees without whose evaluation, encouragement and understanding this work would have been indeed impossible.

Marie Graber

A PRIMER OF
BASIC WINDOW DECORATING
INFORMATION

including a glossary of window fixtures and terms

11

THE HISTORY OF WINDOWS

To our knowledge, no one has established a specific beginning for windows. Probably because man from his earliest days recognized the need to have openings in his dwellings which would permit light and air to enter.

It didn't take him long to recognize another need. His openings had to be closed at times to protect him from elements not so desirable as light and air. He began by rolling a rock in front of the cave opening, or by placing a stone in a crudely chiseled "window".

This first technique of window decorating was little improved by the time of early Colonial America. Then, oiled paper or linen, animal skins, and wood shutters covered the windows for all but the very rich. It wasn't until 1903 that glass panes became commonplace and even these were quite distorted.

Glass first covered windows, as you know, well before this. Early windows were covered not with a single sheet of glass as we know it today, but with several small pieces. At first, these were irregularly shaped and fitted with lead, then later in square shapes or panes. The early panes were distorted and actually made by flattening a bowl or bottlelike glass blowing.

Although Louis Lucas, a French glassmaker, was the first to make plate glass in 1668, it was not used for windows until the 20th century. This was the first non-distorted glass and it was used initially in making mirrors of the highest quality.

Finally, during World War I (1914-1919), a method was developed to mechanically produce sheet glass free from distortions. The technique was developed simultaneously by glassmakers in Europe and in the United States.

Window decorating as we know it today developed much more rapidly than the windows it decorates. At first, its sole purpose was to provide privacy. In Europe, even today, shutters are commonplace. In early America, there was little need, for houses were secure simply because people did not venture out at night. As cities were established and it was safe for men and women to leave their homes at night, the need became apparent, whether the glass was distorted or not.

Most drapery fixtures as we know them today are products of the past 100 years. And many of them were not known ten years ago. Today there is a rebirth of elegance and window decorating does a great deal more than just provide privacy.

BASIC WINDOW TREATMENTS

Why are some paintings featured in museums and others forgotten in the attic? It's all a matter of technique! Here are some basic window decorating techniques which serve as the starting point for the ideas in this book. Properly applied, they can turn your windows into true works of decorating art. If you are now considering a window decorating project and do not recognize your particular situation here, you'll probably find it in "Problem Windows" section (pg. 70).

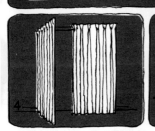

1. ELEGANT TRAVERSE — Pleated custom or ready-made draperies hung from one of the newer decorative brass or aluminum cafe-traverse rods. They are made to be seen and have sculptured finials. Operate with draw cord. This treatment can be achieved with or without rings. Use with picture windows, out-opening

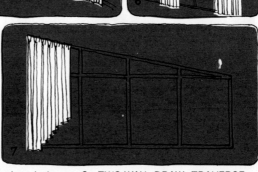

casements, window-walls, jalousie windows. 2. TWO-WAY DRAW TRAVERSE — Draperies open to both sides and close in the middle. Operation and uses are the same as Elegant Traverse, however fixture used is a standard traverse rod. Variations are a combination curtain and traverse fixture using sheer curtains behind draperies, or a double-traverse rod with two sets of traversing fabric. 3. ONE-WAY DRAW TRAVERSE — Drapery draws to either right or left, depending upon installation. Best for corner windows or window walls and side sections of large bay windows. 4. FRENCH DOOR DRAW — This can be used on in-opening casement windows. Traverse fixtures are mounted on door or window frame and swing open and closed with casement or door. 5. BAY TREATMENT — Single expanse of fabric on custom-curved curtain or traverse rods covers the bay window. This is best for the circular bay or bow window. However, you may choose to treat each window in a conventional bay separately. 6. PATIO ROD TREATMENT — A special combination cord plus hand traverse rod is used here, where a window wall is adjoined by a door to a patio or porch. Gives effect of continuous treatment yet allows free and easy access to door when desired. 7. CATHEDRAL TRAVERSE — Also called Trapazoidal Treatment. This uses a one-way draw traverse, opening toward apex of window. Draperies are custom tailored with slanting tops. For only the most modern homes where, for

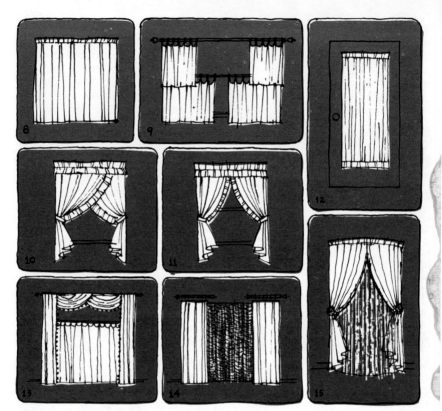

example, the entire wall can be so covered. 8. STATIONARY OR TRAVERSE CURTAINS — Transparent or semi-transparent curtains shirred on a curtain rod, or pleated and hung from a traverse rod. Often hung under draperies. Good for virtually any window type when a variable amount of light and privacy is desired. 9. CAFE CURTAINS/DRAPERIES — May be hung singly or in pairs, in any length. Or stack three or more. Curtains with tailored, scalloped or plain headings are hung from cafe rods with clips, rings or sewn-on loops. Best for picture, double-hung, dormer, bay or window walls. 10. PRISCILLA CURTAINS — Crisp chintz, organdy, or any sheer fabric curtains with extra wide panels are overlapped. Curtains are shirred on double curtain rods. Valance may be added. Particularly suited for bay windows, double-hung and picture windows. 11. PRISCILLA TIEBACK — Fabrics used here should be of a sheer or medium heaviness. Fabric is shirred on a single curtain rod and held back using braided, fabric, or molded decorative tiebacks. For bay, picture, dormer or double-hung windows. 12. SASH CURTAINS — Covering only the glass, curtains are shirred on rods top and bottom, or top only. Use with doors, in-opening casement, ranch, and small jalousie windows. 13. SWAG TREATMENT — This is often used to frame a window for a more elaborate decorative effect. The specially tailored swag (see Unique Ideas section, page 65) is gracefully draped over a decorative aluminum or brass cafe rod or shirred on concealed rod. Ideal for tall, massive windows and arched windows. 14. AUSTRIAN AND ROMAN SHADES — The ultimate in luxury. These are a long way from conventional window shades, but are so called because they gather at the top of the window when opened. Often used with tied-back or traversing draperies for framing. 15. TIEBACK TREATMENT — This is an additional decorative treatment that can be used to determine a period by choice of fabric and design of tiebacks employed. Ideal for double-

14

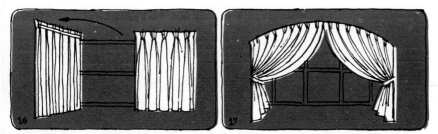

hung windows. 16. DRAPERY CRANE TREATMENT — Used for stationary panels either side of window. An adjustable bracket allows drapery to be swung outward or adjusts horizontally to give the illusion of greater window width. Best solution for in-opening casement windows. Also use with awning or jalousie windows. 17. ARCHED WINDOWS — Prevalent with Spanish or Moorish architecture this can also be used for archways. Requires custom bent overhead fixture conforming to the curve of the arch. You can also hide the arch using a valance, see page 84.

SOME THOUGHTS TO KEEP IN MIND

⁚ you were investigating the purchase of a new family car, your decision would ⸝ertainly be affected by considerations far apart from the car itself. The size of your family, for example, would be important. So, too, in window decorating there are factors to consider aside from the window shape or location.

CLIMATE

Yes, it does make a difference. Climate does not bear heavily on the style of treatment, but it does affect the selection of drapery fixtures. If you live in a

damp, humid area, near water or near the seashore, your air is likely to be laden with corrosive elements. As you know, salt air particularly affects metals and fabrics. You'll have no problem, however, if you select fixtures made from aluminum. They are more costly but will save you money in the long run. The nice thing about it is that today many types of fixtures, even those elegant cafe rods, are available in this wonderful metal.

15

THE SEASONS OF THE YEAR

WINTER   SUMMER

Most of us cannot afford the time or money to have one set of furniture in storage while another is in use, depending upon the season. For years, though, we have used slipcovers particularly during summer months when we wish to change to a cool, light, airy decor. That same idea should be carried on to the draperies to complete the seasonal treatment. Why not have two or more sets of draperies, perhaps a solid color for winter and fall and a colorful airy print for spring and summer? And, going a step further, wouldn't it be grand to have a Poinsettia print for the Christmas season? The cost is little when you think of the pleasure it will provide.

HOW OFTEN DO YOU USE THE WINDOW?

There are undoubtedly some windows in your home that you are constantly opening or closing. How about that one you never open? This affects fixture selection. That little or never used window can be more economically treated with a hand traverse fixture with a baton. The frequently used window demands a cord traverse treatment, perhaps with a cord tension pulley. If extra-wide or heavy fabric is used you will want new electric controls for drapery operation.

THE "YOU" IN DECORATING

This is important. No matter how concise or colorful a window decorating idea may be, it is only an idea without that most important ingredient . . . you! Remember, too, that unless a window treatment truly reflects your personality and tastes, you won't enjoy it. And, after all, your thoughts are the most important.

AN ILLUSTRATED GLOSSARY OF WINDOW FIXTURES AND TERMS

ACCESSORY. Any of a group of products used with drapery fixtures. Tiebacks, braid, tassels, hooks, clips, rings, etc.

16

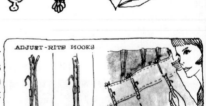

Adjust-rite. Used to describe a particular type of adjustable drapery hook. Adjusts up or down in ¼" increments to straighten the imperfect hem or heading or to adjust for shrinking or stretching of fabric.

ADJUST-RITE HOOKS

Anodized. Special type of aluminum finish, generally in brass, used in the manufacture of certain drapery fixtures.

Apron. That part of a window casing located beneath the sill.

Austrian shades. Actually, draperies which gather at the top of the window by using special hardware.

BATONS. Fiber glass rods with molded handle and clip used to hand traverse draperies. (No cord.)

Bracket. Attaches to wall, casing or ceiling. Receives drapery fixture with slip-in automatic-lock action. Many types and projections.

CAFE ROD. Round fixture made of aluminum, brass or wood. From 9/16″ to 1-3/8″ in diameter. Adjustable length on all except wood. Curtains or draperies attach to rings, ring-clips, or fabric loops.

Cafe-Traverse Rod. Fixture of aluminum, brass, steel or wood that gives full-round appearance identical to cafe rod. Ring slides or plain slides carry draperies and provide cord traverse operation. Both cafe rods and cafe-traverse rods generally have distinctive decorative pole ends and may have smooth or ribbed (fluted) surface. Both also available in different colors. You buy them in assembled or adjustable sets, or have them made-to-measure by your dealer.

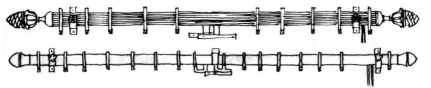

Canopy curtain rod. A special, adjustable fixture for creation of awning or canopy treatments.

Carrier. Usually molded, may be metal, with or without ball bearings. It moves in the rod and holds the hook to which fabric is attached. Allow one carrier for each pleat except at master slide and corner of drapery.

Casing. Part of a window that fits into the wall, generally concealed with a wide molding.

17

Cord Traverse. Refers to conventional method of opening and closing draperies by pulling a cord.

Cord tension pulley. An accessory mounted on the floor or wall which keeps cord taut and off the floor. Particularly desirable for wide windows.

Curtain rod. A non-traversing fixture made of steel or aluminum with curtains generally shirred on or may be pinned on. Purchased in adjustable sets or made-to-measure by your dealer. Special types for bay windows, corner windows, etc.

Custom. Same as made-to-measure. Refers to any fixture specially assembled by a dealer and tailored to exact requirements of the drapery treatment.

DECORATIVE RODS. Term used to distinguish newer elegant cafe-type fixtures from rods of conventional design. Made to be shown and become integral part of decorative effect desired.

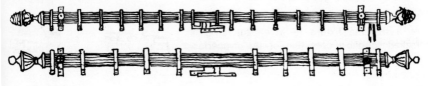

Double rods. Also called multiple rods. Basic feature: two or more rods mounted on one set of brackets. Available in many combinations of plain, traverse or cafe rods. E.g. traverse and valance; two curtain rods, etc.

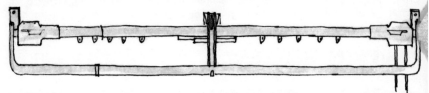

Drapery crane. Used to hang side panels. The bracket can incorporate features that allow for wider window effects and variable projections.

Draw drapery. Common terminology for cord traverse.

EXTENDER. Any device used to lengthen a fixture or bracket.

FRAME. The part that holds the glass in a window.

Fringe. Used for trimming draperies or shades.

HEAVY DUTY. Term used to describe fixtures designed to support fabrics of medium to heavy weights.

Holdback. Any accessory that holds draperies to side of window. Often allows for release so drapery can hang as a straight panel when desired. Usually ornate. Many types of finishes and generally of brass or molded materials.

Hook. An accessory sewn, pinned, or slipped into the drapery heading for hanging on slide carriers or cafe rings. Also hooks directly over rod to support drapery or valance.

JABOT. Vertical fabric sections in a swag drapery treatment.

LINED DRAPERIES. Any drapery with a double thickness of fabric. The inner fabric is frequently an off-white or neutral color. It is a protection against fading and stops sunlight.

Lock seam. Type of curtain rod seam that provides extra rigidity together with a plastic threading thimble that protects fabric from tears when putting curtain on rod.

MASTER SLIDES. The large over-lapping arms of a traverse fixture to which the cord is locked to allow operation of the draperies.

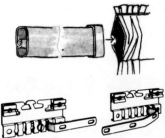

OVAL RODDING. Heavy gauge steel rodding small in dimension. It is cut-to-size required for curtains, valance and cafe rods.

PANEL. A single section of drapery.

Pleating Tape. The perfect way to make draperies at home. The tape eliminates measuring and permits the homemaker to make professional looking pleats with no chance for error. Pleats are automatically measured.

Projection. The distance between the back of a rod and the wall or casing. Special brackets can provide as much as a seven inch projection, needed when draperies must clear air conditioner, etc.

RECESSED. Term applied to mounting inside window casing or dormer. Also mounted in ceiling so that rod is always concealed.

Ring slide. Combination slide with decorative ring used on cafe-traverse rods.

SHIRRED. Curtains inserted on a rod by pushing the fixture through a pre-sewn pocket in the fabric.

Shirring tape. Half-inch wide tape with woven-in loops and herringbone cotton pull for Austrian shades or valances.

Sill. Horizontal platform at the bottom of a window.

Spring Tension Rod. Oval or round rod which is installed inside window casing or dormer. It holds its position by pressure, no brackets or screws are used.

Supports. Mounting devices may be wall or ceiling mounted. Number required is dictated by weight of fabric, span and surface on which mounted.

19

TASSELS. Accessories used for trimming.

Tiebacks. Decorative and functional accessories for accenting and holding drapery. Molded designs, braided cords or fabric loops are used alone or combined.

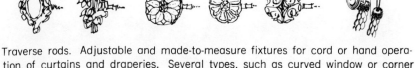

Traverse rods. Adjustable and made-to-measure fixtures for cord or hand operation of curtains and draperies. Several types, such as curved window or corner rods. Operation varies, too, from rods which operate in one direction to rods which operate several panels by pulling one cord.

UNLINED DRAPERIES. Draperies with a single thickness of fabric.

VALANCE. Short, decorative drapery across the top of a window.

WEIGHTS. Lead in various shapes or tape form sewn into the base of a drapery panel to aid in more graceful hanging.

Window widener. A special fixture used to achieve wider window effects.

WINDOWS FOR
LIVING ROOMS AND
FAMILY ROOMS

20

THE RETURN TO ELEGANCE

At no other time in our history has the world of interior decorating been so excitingly alive. In every segment of interior planning the products of today's technology sing out for attention and get it. What's new today may be even newer tomorrow. We're caught in a surprisingly pleasant whirlwind of brilliance. A new decorating verve is here, and it's here to stay!

The "return to elegance" has arrived, my friend, and we're all part of it and liking it. It's natural that in mankind's most prosperous and productive hours he should turn to the splendor once reserved only for kings. We're mixing and matching periods and color has become the mirror of our mood. Bright. Alive. Changing. From London's Carnaby Street to Hollywood's Sunset Drive to your street and my street the mode is madly elegant and properly supreme. Everyone is living in a great new age of interior decorating spawned by the wedding of today's materials and knowledge to yesterday's masterpieces.

On the pages that follow, you will see this new elegant motif portrayed in many new and exciting window treatment ideas. Ideas that employ new and uniquely different decorative drapery fixtures, patterned and styled expressly for the "return to elegance."

WELCOME TO THE NEW WORLD OF ELEGANCE

Dress your picture window in the dramatic new look of elegance. Here is a tasteful combination of classic Florentine charm, the decorator touch of luxury, with beautiful double tiers of sheer or opaque draw draperies.

Using the new 1⅜" fluted cafe-traverse rod for both tiers, you'll have the light and privacy control of a traverse rod. What's more, these new rods go with virtually every mood, modern, traditional, English, Mediterranean, you name it. Even more intriguing is the choice you can make of brass, antiqued brass, decorator or antique white finishes on these tarnish-resistant fixtures.

Select 1⅜" packaged decorative cafe-traverse sets in five lengths for windows up to 4, 6, 8, 10, or 12 feet in width. Or, select an adjustable style, also available in black and walnut wood tone.

22

Or, you can make your cafes go formal in this evening gown length to enrich the comfortable mood of the room. The corner windows complement each other with the generously pleated cafes hung in the two-tier treatment. They're subtly accented by the smooth, unbroken lines and exquisite pineapple or classic design pole ends of those new cafe-traverse rods.

For a variation of the previous two treatments, try this idea. You'll achieve the ultimate in the new look of elegance without overstating and you'll retain the privacy and charm of the tiered effect. Substitute a 1⅜" fluted decorative adjustable cafe rod at the top, add a pair of braided rayon cord mini-tiebacks, or any one of several tiebacks or holdbacks in a harmonizing design and matching finish.

23

The classic symbols of comfortable living are simply stated by applying wallpaper in a lacy grillwork effect around a cafe-clad window. A wonderful idea for windows like this is the inside casing mount allowing the draperies to fall within the casing and create this appealing framed effect.

It's done with cut-to-measure brass tubing held in place by the new adjustable brass tension sockets. This effort saving and handsome technique eliminates brackets and screws.

To really change the mood of a room, give your principal window that quaint, rustic look with a decorative traverse rod, adjustable or made-to-measure. Top it off with shutters stained or painted to match. You can choose any finish. And how much more striking and massive this will appear if 1⅜" diameter rods are used! The authentic richness of real wood poles is available in strong vinyl clad steel in wood tones. The convenience of traverse action makes this a truly practical treatment as well as stunning in appearance.

24

Here's an attractive variation for tall, modern corner windows where plenty of light and privacy are prime concerns. The vertical segmented lines of the window grouping are complemented by gleaming brass finish spring-tension cafe rods holding deeply scalloped cafe curtains. It's so easy to adjust to any curtain length because this rod moves up and down as needed, yet holds firmly wherever you set it. Select spring tension cafe rods adjustable

up to 84"; or, cut-to-measure brass tubing with brass cafe rings and adjustable brass tension sockets. And the practical beauty is further enhanced, for you don't have to put any screws in the wood frame!

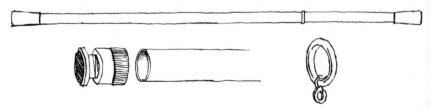

Among the many decorative treatments of windows you often find flanking a fireplace or bookcase is this exquisitely fresh and formal treatment, tastefully done with the elegant flair to create a pleasing balance while accentuating and flattering the natural focal point of the room. Draperies are hung from fluted adjustable cafe rods and sweep softly back to reveal filmy sheer under draperies on one-way adjustable traverse rods.

The pleasing dimension of the treatment is established by employing new adjustable braided cord tiebacks. The cord encircles the drapery panel and attaches to an exposed decorative mini-tieback or a cup hook out of sight beneath the drapery. For maximum light or view the sheers can be opened. For another mood, simply remove one end of the braid from the hook, allowing the draperies to fall and create complete privacy.

For the popular Colonial or Traditional effect on two ordinary long windows, here's a treatment that complements your good taste both inside and out while making your room seem larger and ceilings higher. From ¾" or 1" gleaming brass cafe rods with matching rings, hang an overdrapery from the top window casing. The panels cascade to matching solid brass tiebacks or molded tiebacks in a Federal Eagle design aligned just above the sill and then to the floor. Aligned with the tiebacks, another ¾" or 1" brass cafe rod, with rings, supports matching or contrasting cafe curtains to the floor.

Where the view outside is not important, filter the light through pleated or shirred-on sheer under curtains dramatized by bands of fabric in an accent color strung taut between two 1⅜" tarnish-resistant adjustable cafe rods. A truly elegant, fashion-right touch which can be used equally well with either stationary or traversing draperies behind to create a window where there isn't any. Or, to disguise a window that doesn't merit attention otherwise.

This massive wall-to-wall "window" is actually two windows. Here, they take on all the leading elements of decorative interest to change the mood of the entire room and reflect the vibrant colors and elegant continental treatment so much in fashion today. The large diameter adjustable cafe rod with massive rings accentuates this interesting treatment. You can choose black, fine wood tone, antique brass, antique white, or decorator white for the finish on the rod. The flowing lines of draperies and rod together are accented by the interesting rose cluster design holdback. Behind the boldly swept back and stationary center panels, a two-way draw adjustable traverse rod supports contrasting draperies to complete the setting and offer flexibility of exposure and privacy.

Adjust to the weather! The wonderful flexibility of this treatment allows you to use a gay print on the three front panels so that with two panels held back, you let in the summer sun and breeze through the traversing sheer. Dropped, they conceal the winter drabness and cold.

Select from ¹⁵⁄₁₆″ or 1⅜″ adjustable or made-to-measure cafe rods in the newer decorative designs for the outside panels. The inside sheer drapery is traversed on a two-way draw rod. The holdbacks are rose cluster design. For more unique decorating effects, select rings in choice of matching or contrasting finishes.

Discriminating use of wallpaper with ceiling-to-floor draperies make this window a focal point in any room. Use it in an otherwise bland room to create interest or to break up the monotonous, uninteresting long wall. Use the same wallpaper under sill and above casing of window and on adjacent wall.

Select two-way draw adjustable traverse rod in one of five extensions from 30″ to 224″. Self-locking slide-in brackets allow you to mount this type of rod on any casing or wall flush to the ceiling to get the ceiling-to-floor draped effect.

27

The contemporary or "ranch style" picture window is in for a fashion surprise. This one looks its best framed by wall-to-wall, ceiling-to-floor draperies. For suburbanites and city apartment dwellers alike this treatment is far more attractive than simply hanging your draperies, window-wide, from the top casing of the window. The ceiling-to-floor drapery makes the room seem more spacious, more luxurious. It is especially good for the placement of large pieces of furniture, since the draperies provide a neutral background.

For the ultimate in convenience and luxury motorize your traverse draperies! That's right, today's technology has produced a wonderful remote control that allows you to automatically open or close your draperies to any desired position at the touch of a button. Particularly practical for large areas of drapery or heavy draperies. Especially helpful where furniture placement, for example, makes it inconvenient to reach windows easily. (It can be had with remote control!) You can install it yourself easily in minutes, however, if you are planning a new home have your contractor install the wiring with wall switch-type operation.

Do a uniquely fresh switch on the usual double drapery ceiling-to-floor treatment and achieve this interesting effect. Hang your stationary or traverse draperies in one of the delightful new printed sheers under plain over draperies in a contrasting color. Select either double-traverse for a double set of traversing draperies or combination traverse and plain rod for stationary sheer draperies under the traversing draperies.

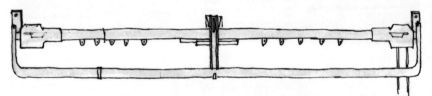

There's something about fresh, crisp curtains that makes a house a home — comfortable, inviting and warm. Perfect for the Cape Cod house, the early American decor or, for change of pace anywhere, select from these treatments.

Criss-Cross Curtains. Hang curtains as shown on adjustable double curtain rods, extensions from 28″ to 120″. At wider windows, use two 28″ rod extenders.

Priscilla Curtains with Valance. Hang curtains as illustrated using casing mounted double rod. Mount curtains on the inside rod and the valance on the outside rod.

Corner Criss-Cross or Priscilla Curtains. Hang three panels of priscilla type curtains as shown. Center panel is hung on both sections of single adjustable corner rod for windows 28″ to 48″ wide. Rod is supplied complete with brackets for corner mounting.

No matter what the decor, you can depend on this treatment to harmonize with its surroundings. It uses conventional two-way draw draperies with matching or contrasting valance. Simply hang your draperies on the rear two-way traverse section of a combination adjustable traverse and valance rod. The valance then shirrs onto valance rod or hangs over the rod using adjust-rite hooks to adjust valance to desired height.

Winning ways with windows in your home

DINING ROOM AND KITCHEN

Have you ever wondered why even the most common meal is somehow more enjoyable in a fine restaurant, while your most epicurean efforts at home sometimes seem lacking? There's a lot more to it than not having to do the preparation yourself. The proper setting is more important, and obviously we don't mean where to place the silver. Your dining areas can have that ring of opulence through window treatments that are fashion-right.

Here's a delightfully fashionable window for your dining room or dining area. You'll be enchanted by the elegant simplicity of the delicately fluted cafe rods with pineapple finials. This unique drapery treatment can be carried out over any window, sliding glass doors — even a blank wall! And the pineapple, you know, is the symbol of hospitality.

The gay panel draperies in front are easily made of either a striped or bright solid color material. Using a 2 or 3 inch spacing, make alternate, loosely hanging loops to extend about 3 inches above the body of the drapery with the rod inserted through loops. Behind, you may wish to have sheer traverse draperies.

A variation on this theme can be accomplished for the ultimate in opulence through the addition of a lavish expanse of shirred Austrian shades instead of the draw draperies. The plain over draperies are hung from elegant cafe rods complete with massive fluted rings. The final touch is the addition of sculptured tiebacks, one on each side. Use 1⅜" adjustable cafe rods and two-way adjustable traverse rod for the initial treatment. For the variation, use cafe rods and substitute Austrian shade tape and hardware for the traverse rod. (For making Austrian shades, see Sewing Section, Page 95.)

High ceilings with high windows demand a look of elegance. Here's a pair of high fashion treatments for those high windows done with the latest decorator-inspired cafe rodding and luxurious swag draperies.

Use long lengths of heavy drapery material for the outer swag type draperies edged with fringe or tassels and permanently pleated as shown. Under cafe draperies of matching or contrasting material are deeply-scooped or traversing cafes, as you prefer. Select the new 1⅜" adjustable cafe rod or cut-to-measure rodding without rings for the swags. Project rod out from casing or wall to its maximum, allowing jabot to hang over under draperies. Under draperies are hung from either 1" adjustable cafe rods or from 1⅜" adjustable cafe traverse rods with ring slides. For the unusually wide window, your dealer can prepare cut-to-measure rods. Swags and their preparation with the convenient new swag tapes are fully described in the Unique Ideas and Sewing Sections.

Fresh as the morning sunrise is this breakfast corner with sheer panel curtains and shirred valance of the same or contrasting material. All you need is a combination valance and traverse rod. Both rods are installed on one set of brackets, supplied complete, the front rod holds the valance and the rear rod the traversing draperies.

Here's a kitchen cafe treatment that will look fresh, new and bright, years from the day you put it up, thanks to aluminum adjustable cafe rods with brass finish. Tarnish-resistant, what a blessing, they're available in diameters from ½" to 1⅜" and are adjustable up to 120" or more. Anchor your cafes top and bottom with anodized aluminum cafe clips to the adjustable cafe rods. These cafe clips will not only hold the curtain in taut folds, but will also allow you to easily remove the curtains for laundering. To coordinate that nearby kitchen door window, repeat the procedure.

33

A touch of Paris or Greenwich Village — this continental sidewalk cafe treatment brings the outside indoors with a gay patio awning shading a planter. You can use a sash rod on top and a canopy curtain rod with 8" projection on the bottom of the awning.

Here are four new ideas for the typical over-the-sink kitchen window designed to offer both privacy and daylight plus that all important view of the children at play, or a relaxing out-of-doors scene. First, a basic treatment employing inexpensive ready-made shirred or pleated valances on a pair of spring tension rods give a new look to your kitchen, yet leave woodwork unmarred. No brackets.

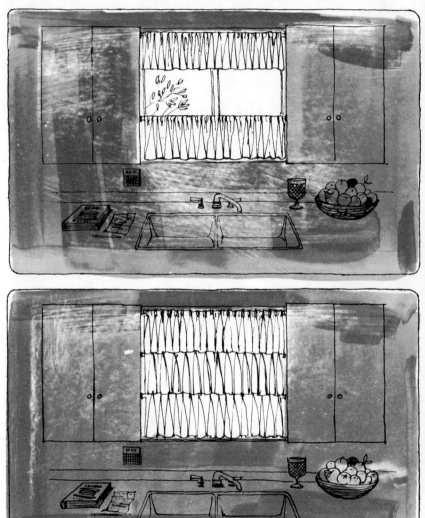

Give your window a ruffled effect by using three pleated valances on three spring tension rods. You may alter the effect by replacing the bottom two valances with a cafe curtain hung on the middle spring tension rod with cafe clips. Or, attach all three valances by cafe-clip rings instead of shirring onto the spring tension rods. The latter two variations will allow you to open valances or curtains as you choose, singly or in pairs.

Here's a similar treatment, but this time the top valances are replaced by the hinged wood shutters, painted to pick up the accent colors in a colonial or country kitchen. The spring tension rod allows you to use full-length shutters accented by the richness of fabric. Spring tension rod is placed just inside cabinet edges, permitting shutters to be opened without disturbing curtain.

This treatment, for deep shadow-box type ranch windows, uses the larger diameter ¾" cut-to-measure rodding in brass finish inside casing with matching rings and held tightly in place by the new adjustable brass tension socket.

And here's a neat trick you can do to add a touch of elegance to your kitchen decor and be practical at the same time. A pair of decorative sculptured hold-backs or tiebacks measuring 3½" across make eye catching towel holders. They are tarnish-proof and available in many hand-crafted designs finished in antique brass, antique white and nutmeg.

That boxed-in kitchen window can take on a new, neat and clean appearance without great expense. Shirred curtains, one (center) panel is sheer and crisp and two (side) panels in gay patterned material are slipped onto two oval spring tension rods mounted top and bottom to the inside of the window casing. For windows from 16" to 84" wide, this one is also ideal for windows boxed-in by cabinets top and sides.

Put a charming double apron on your tall, narrow window, to give a wider, more massive effect, with a spring-tension cafe rod set into the top of the window casing, and a lovely large round adjustable cafe-traverse rod with tarnish-resistant brass finish mounted outside of the window for the lower tier. Choose contrasting or matching materials and deeply scooped pleating. Use a spring-tension cafe rod in brass for upper rod and cafe rings of your choice for the top and cafe-traverse bottom or apron rod. With this treatment, you have the convenience of hand-operated cafes or traverse cafes as you choose.

37

A chic treatment for those double kitchen or dining room windows, light and airy with an exciting elegant flair. Select two of the differently new 1⅜" fluted and adjustable cafe rods with matching fluted rings and classic pineapple finials. Mount as shown in the illustration and hang three cafe panels on top and one using matching material extending the full length of the windows, at the mid-point of the window. Center top panel is hung behind outside panels, doubling up on the rings as shown. A simple matching fabric tieback to cinch in the curtains completes this striking ensemble.

For a practical, balanced kitchen window treatment, go to simple double cafe curtains or cafe-valance combination on two demure ¾" or smaller tarnish-resistant adjustable cafe rods. Top rod holds ruffled valance while lower rod supports full half-window cafes, all done in a cheerful patterned material; or, try contrasting print cafes and a solid color valance. Select decorative or plain cafe clips for your rods.

Disguise and "cozyize" your breakfast nook or dining ell with corner window arrangement by employing this unique, decorator inspired treatment. Use drapery material that matches your wallpaper or paper your wall with the fabric! You'll like the convenience and ease of operating curved two-way draw or a pair of one-way draw traverse rods.

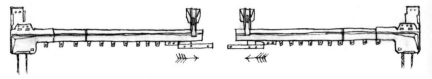

If you are blessed with antiques in your dining room or dining area, you'll want to carry out the antique theme in your window treatment to accent the timeless character of your prized pieces. If your dominant furniture pieces (table, chairs or buffet) are painted, select a 1⅜" plain or reeded cut-to-measure wood pole with matching wood rings and authentic turned pole ends in unfinished wood. Then paint the rod and rings to match the furniture.

If your dominant pieces are brass or accented by brass you may want to select one of the newer aluminum adjustable cafe rods in antique brass finish.

The antique valance shown in this treatment is easily fabricated using ½" plywood, cut to the desired shape. Then cover it with fabric, simply stapled or tacked to the back. The completed valance is then fastened directly to the window casing.

Dress up your kitchen doors, back doors, patio doors, French doors — even your garage doors with fresh, crisp shirred curtains using the versatile locked-seam sash rods for windows from 12" to 50" wide. Here are four treatments:

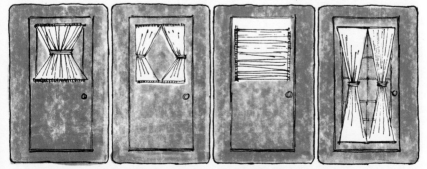

A. Hour Glass. B. Reversed Hour Glass. C. Side-to-side (mount sash rods vertically on sides of door). D. Double Hour Glass (for full-length door windows). Where unusual strength of rod is needed, use cut-to-measure oval rodding with sash brackets. Choose white or brass finish.

BEDROOM WINDOWS

A RETURN TO ELEGANCE FOR THE MASTER BEDROOM

Leading designers and home furnishings editors are all talking about the emergence of the master bedroom as a focal point for the return to elegance in interior decor. You spend one-third of your life there, so it's not surprising that this is the ideal spot to go "all out" with new, unique and exciting coordinated window dressing ideas.

Here, for example, is a dramatic treatment with the elegant flair that works equally well on the bedroom window grouping, a single window or even a bare wall! The ideal start for your own Presidential suite! Light under draperies can be stationary or traversible. Rich and luxurious stationary over draperies, suspended from beautifully fluted decorative cafe rods are tied back by a detailed rose cluster tieback-holdback matching the antique brass finish of the rods. Adjustable cafe rods are mounted with maximum bracket projection to allow the over draperies to hang without interfering with traversing under draperies.

41

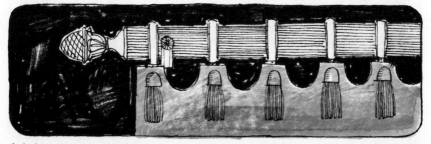

A bold accent to the luxury bedroom decor is matching or contrasting tassels sewn on drapery headings. Today, tassels are available in a rainbow of decorator colors, from gold to avocado. They are charming in contrast to the 1″ or 1⅜″ adjustable decorative cafe-traverse rods in fine woodgrain, antique brass, antique white, black or decorator white. This is a theme easily adapted to any bedroom to change to the new look of elegance. You can even use existing draperies and give them a totally new effect!

Carry your change to elegance a step further. Sew tassels to a dust ruffle on the bed and on the bedside chair and your most inexpensive transition to a coordinated luxury decor is complete! For the window, select the new 1⅜" fluted and antiqued cafe traverse rod sets with decorative high-fashion pole ends, in adjustable lengths. For extra wide windows, have your dealer make-to-measure 1⅜" cafe-traverse rodding.

If you want a bedroom that cleverly combines all of the latest ideas in the elegant mode plus the practical advantages of privacy and light control, you'll love this idea. That wonderful Florentine flair reflecting the Corinthian column and ageless lines of Old World designs is portrayed with luxurious sheer satin Austrian shades hanging in neat rows of miniature folds to the floor. Over draperies cascade in generous side folds to sculptured holdbacks, finished in antique brass or antique white to match the elegant cafe rods with massive rings. Using the same material, a flowing swag held by three matching tiebacks adorns the wall over the bed and completes a most high fashion grouping.

Three cheers for tiers and the many decorative effects you can achieve with these versatile showy curtains. Bank them dramatically around the corner of a room on brass cafe rods as shown, disguising high ranch-type windows and bringing them into closer touch with your furniture grouping.

Checkerboard cafe curtains are charming in a child's room. If you use the reversible kind, you'll be able to vary the combination at will as in the printed tier combined with the plain tier. Tarnish-resistant cafe rods in antiqued finishes will never need attention, give you years of sparkling beauty and charm.

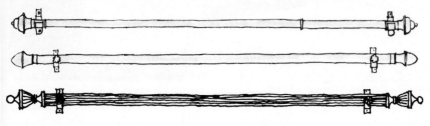

Send a cheery valance marching around the room on adjustable corner curtain rods. In this interesting treatment, the coordinated valance-drapery and dust ruffle pulls the entire room together. The valance also serves the purpose of decorating the high strip ranch-type windows without interfering with light and air circulation from outside.

For corner-and-wall type valance, select a single adjustable corner curtain rod. Curtain rod extender can be added for large spans or have your dealer cut-to-measure oval rodding with reversible elbows at corner. For stationary drapery over bed that creates this unusual headboard effect, select single adjustable curtain rod with 1½" projection to fit smoothly beneath valance.

44

Be ultra feminine with this chic bedroom treatment. Perfect for the sugar and spice set from 2 to 20. It's row upon row of "cool" ruffles with plain traversing over draperies. Simply shirr your rows of ruffles individually and sew them onto one window-size piece of the same material to be gathered on the plain curtain rod of a combination traverse and plain rod set. Repeat the ruffles and flourishes on your bedspread.

For an extra special coordinating touch to this treatment, turn your bed into a canopy bed using four 1⅜" cut-to-measure reeded wood poles and cut-to-measure rodding. Top the poles with authentic turned wood pole ends and shirr your ruffles onto the rod all the way around, or hang it with fabric loops or rings. Poles are anchored by bolts or heavy screws to bed frame. Paint or stain the poles to match your furniture.

Whether your bedroom window is directly over the bed or for an extra special effect to coordinate your room, spotlighting the bed, try one of these.

Take a matching bedspread and double drapery set and team them up with over drape swept back to decorative brass tiebacks for this charmingly simple effect designed to give even an inexpensive Hollywood bed dramatic importance. The wall behind the bed can also be painted in an accent color or covered with stationary draperies if a double curtain rod is used.

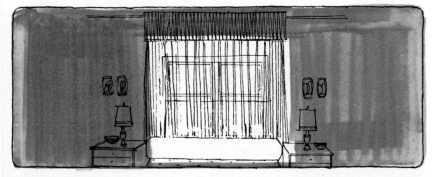

45

A simple traverse-valance rod mounted ceiling height or lower above your bed produces this smooth, contemporary shallow canopy effect. A shirred or pleated valance goes on the outside rod while the traversing draperies hide high ranch-type or double-hung window behind. Open them during the day or night for light and a breeze. Close them for privacy and a warm, comfortable mood.

Illustrated at top of next page is a pleasant touch to the behind-the-bed treatment. Build a bold valance, generously scalloped. Hang stationary drapery panels in contrasting material at each end of the valance and finish the setting with a strategically placed picture or picture grouping for the wall between the panels. A good spot for those favorite portraits of the children!

Build the valance using ½" plywood nailed or screwed and glued with 1" x 2" blocks in each corner. Stretch fabric over board and tack to back side. Select cut-to-measure curtain rodding and fasten to inside of valance with brackets about 2" to 3" from wall. Valance, completely assembled, can be fastened to wall with sturdy angle iron braces.

With the "return to elegance" comes the return to the exciting and glamorous canopy beds of the Victorian era, improved in appearance and practicality through the use of modern fabrics and fixtures. This example is sure to bring compliments and it's a decorating delight because the rods save you work, expense, and elaborate carpentry yet you achieve the authentic look. It can be removed for laundering in seconds!

Drape the luxurious material as shown above taking one end all the way to the floor behind the bed. Add tassels and scallops. Select four 1⅜" diameter fluted adjustable cafe rods. Each rod is suspended from the ceiling using two cup hooks screwed into the ceiling using plaster plugs, if needed, and two fluted massive cafe rings to match the rod finish you select.

The elegant bed canopy you see here belies its simple foundation, oval rodding put together by your dealer to the dimensions you desire. Side draperies hang on inside rod (see diagram), valance on the outside.

Here's a coordinated bedroom idea that combines the lush extravagance of the high fashion elegance trend with the practical, uncluttered approach of the modern and contemporary decor which employs a careful choice of furnishings and colors. Window drapery panels are stationary on single adjustable curtain rod. Simple fabric tieback of the same·material with matching embroidered edge is held by those new rose cluster tiebacks. Easy fold-up Roman shades complete the treatment. See Sewing Section for instructions.

Ceiling-mounted cut-to-measure rodding provides the shape and support for the rich and lovely bed treatment. The four drapery panels are made of material to match the window draperies and are lined with the contrasting material used for the tailored bedspread. Tassel-fringe purchased by the yard in color desired, is glued to the rod between panels to hide the rod and complete this ensemble.

Winning ways with windows in your home

BATHROOMS

48

The Presidential Suite continues with elegance in the bathroom. Behind the classic form and beauty of the return to elegance lie many practical ideas creating a whole new mood of luxury compatible with the latest designs in bathroom fixtures and accessories.

Here's a coordinated bathroom ensemble featuring many ways to use those new gleaming brass or antiqued adjustable cafe rods. A 1⅜" decorative adjustable cafe rod is used in the shower recess with matching fluted rings to support both clear shower curtain which falls inside the tub and the decorative draperies hanging to the floor outside the tub. Rod is attached between side walls of recess using 1⅜" pole sockets. Select new 1⅜" adjustable cafe-traverse sets for bathroom windows, and 1⅜" adjustable cafe rods for towel bars. For less massive, more petite towel bars, select smaller diameter rods from ½" up to 1".

Matching fluted adjustable cafe rods with exquisitely reproduced classic or pineapple finials are ideal as towel bars. Best of all, these rods are perfect for all bathroom applications, for they are made of wonderful aluminum, totally unaffected by steam and water for the ultimate in bathroom beauty and service.

A novel idea for lowering that high shower-tub recess is simply done with a neat valance shirred onto two spring tension rods or brass tubing in ¾″ or 1″ diameter using brass tension sockets. Neither technique requires brackets or screws. Valance can be custom-made to drop just below shower curtain rod in fabric that matches or contrasts with your shower curtain.

Today's decorator shower curtain rings in your choice of ten or more colors are designed for distinctive bathroom beauty and performance. You can even match tile or bathroom fixtures, and match or contrast the finishes on those new fluted aluminum cafe rods. These rings can be used with all types of rodding!

If your dressing area or powder room is located where traffic routes interfere with privacy, try this treatment using a gleaming brass cafe rod or fluted cafe rod antiqued in the finish you choose, held by new brass tension sockets, mounted inside the door casing or between two walls. Hang fabric with your choice of cafe rings and clips.

Spangles, bangles and tassels, generously draped to frame the bath recess, and a matching treatment for the windows. Festooned traversing over drapery, elegantly trimmed is swept back on each side to new hand-crafted tiebacks. Practical shower curtain of plastic or another waterproof material is concealed behind.

Brass cafe rods provide the clean luxury accent that takes your bathroom out of the ordinary into a class all by itself. Carry the colorful striped and fringed criss-cross cafes almost to the ceiling to balance the high bath recess. The adjustable brackets on your cafe rods allow you to project out to 3". Add another for your towel bar and you have a beautifully coordinated bathroom. Leaf design holdbacks will add that just-right accent of high fashion to complete the conversion.

Winning ways with windows in your home

APARTMENT WINDOWS

For the past several years, convenient apartment living has become a symbol of the successful elegant trend. And whether you are newly-married and renting, or a silver-anniversaryite owning your apartment in condominium fashion, your windows hold out a particularly inviting challenge. Here, for certain, is the one area where your imagination need not be restricted by the rules set by the building management. No matter what they are, there's a practical way around them at your windows.

Here's an idea to bypass any restrictions on wallpaper or wall color. As you know, many apartments have one basic wall color, beige or off-white, at best your color selection is often limited to a few pastels. Let's add the richness of fabric in any color or pattern we choose to an entire wall!

53

And there need not even be a window behind these elegant draperies. Select two-way draw traverse set, adjustable up to 224″ and mount it to ceiling. For stationary draperies, have your dealer cut-to-measure oval rodding.

Here's how you can turn an ordinary two-way draw traverse treatment into a fetching fenestration that will make your apartment the focal point of other tenants' admirations. Select a bracket and valance kit to convert ordinary traverse rods into combination valance and traverse rods. You save expense here, for often apartment owners have the builder install ordinary traverse rods. Let your imagination be your guide in selecting a valance of contrasting solid color or complementing print, trim it with fringe or tassels if you like.

Want to make a window appear wider with a high-fashion look, but you're not permitted to mount your rods anywhere but on the casing? Here's the solution, select a window-wider adjustable traverse rod. This unique fixture has special brackets that attach to the casing, yet the rod extends to either side of the window. Special bumpers protect the wall. If you already have your traverse rod, or it has been installed by the building, ask for a build-on kit.

Make a fluted frame for that picture window with new massive 1⅜" fluted decorative cafe rods with matching rings mounted on top and bottom of the window. Select 1⅜" decorative adjustable cafe rods with matching rings in antique brass, antique white, woodgrain, black or decorator white finish.

Apartment dwellers will like this idea when space is at a premium and it's a perfect idea for drying those overnight washables. Just hang them on tarnish-resistant ¾" cafe rodding, cut-to-measure by your dealer and mounted in the bath-shower recess using two adjustable brass tension sockets. Easy to put up and easy to take down whenever you need it, uses no screws.

If you're lucky enough to have a terrace or porch off your apartment, here's an opportunity for the ultimate in high fashion elegance. Stripe up the band with tassel-fringe and flags in a uniquely different Roman shade accented by cafe rods. Select adjustable decorator cafe rods in antique brass finish with classic finials for use in pockets sewn-in at the top and bottom of the shade. Top rod is decorative but bottom rod also serves functional purpose since the shade is always weighted at this point. You may complete the ensemble by repeating stripes and fringe on table linen. See Sewing Section, Page 110, for Roman Shade instructions.

56

Oh how lovely that terrace or balcony is, especially when a wonderful new combination door and window traverse rod lets us use it without fighting to open the door. In this practical and long-awaited treatment, a single door and window traverse rod allows us to cover with one expanse of fabric both window wall and door. The picture window or window wall section of this rod is a two-way cord draw traverse operation. It can be operated by standard pull-cords. The part covering the door is a hand-traverse operation, opened when you want access to the door with a baton to protect drapery from soiling. Both sections operate independently of each other, so you can open window or door draperies separately or together as you choose. Same rod can be adjusted for doors to right or left of the window.

Here's a variation on the door and window traverse treatment, this time adding the timeless value of a valance. Select an adjustable or cut-to-measure curtain rod, mounted 2″ or 3″ above the door and window traverse rod. High enough so the valance will clear the top of the door when it is opened, yet completely conceal the second rod. What a trim, complete and coordinated effect this achieves.

UNIQUE IDEAS
FOR THE
CLEVER HOMEMAKER

On the following pages you'll find a collection of unique and original ideas for decorating throughout your home with drapery fixtures, plus helpful hints and illustrated information on how to make some of the curtain and drapery applications seen elsewhere in this book. Perhaps you'll find in this collection of odd jobs for rods the answer to a long-standing decorating problem.

Here is an interesting room divider idea that can be easily developed using seamless brass tubing in 1″ and 1½″ diameters or the cut-to-measure 1⅜″ plain or fluted aluminum tubing in various antiqued finishes. Your dealer can cut-to-measure the lengths required and provide mounting hardware. This simple pole-type divider can be accomplished by any do-it-yourselfer in a few minutes. The tubing selected should be cut to ceiling height, less ¾″. Place new brass tension sockets on each end of each pole and adjust to give tight fit between floor and ceiling.

It was once called window dressing, today it's window decorating, but dressing is still accurate. Especially when you consider that decorating a window is much like dressing ourselves. We want to be in fashion. And window treatments become ever more fashion-right thanks to the wonderful new products available to us. One of these is the new adjustable brass tension socket. Seamless brass tubing is fitted on both ends with an adjustable socket for a variety of uses. The socket can be adjusted a full ¾ inch.

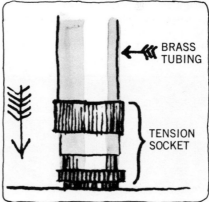

BRASS TUBING

TENSION SOCKET

Wave your baton and a wall appears! A cut-to-measure length of punched over-head track with overhead slides is all you need for this warm, inviting room divider or hide-away wall of draperies. Track mounts directly to ceiling and dra-peries can be stationary or hand traverse operation with the addition of a flexible fiber glass baton to protect drapery from soiling.

Mount shirred curtains of the same color as your draperies or bedspread on the inside of cabinet or closet doors as shown for an unusual decorator touch. This high-fashion idea is achieved with adjustable curtain rods mounted on inside of door frame to hold the panels in place, yet allow them to be easily removed for cleaning or laundering. Why not have a contrasting set to alter the mood?

If you have a talented woodworker around the house, these unique headboards can be made with simple fine wood frames and cut-to-measure seamless brass tubing with matching pole ends. Or, try the new fluted decorative cafe rods with classic or pineapple pole ends for an exquisite decorator headboard.

Here's a real challenge to the homemaker-innovator, a striking accent to any window, the projected awning type valance is the latest idea for the luxurious decor. And today's fixtures make this treatment both easy and economical to have in your home.

Beautifully pleated tieback curtains are shirred on an adjustable locked-seam sash rod mounted to top of window casing using sash brackets. Awning is fabricated of matching or contrasting material with three stitched-in pockets, A, B, C, as illustrated. Sash rods are then inserted, one each, in pockets A and B. The top two rods are then fastened to the wall, above the window, as shown. Poles are cut-to-measure wood poles with authentic turned pole ends. Poles are mounted to wall using inside sockets, and to a cut-to-measure length of seamless brass tubing inserted in pocket C of the awning by inside sockets.

61

Here's a variation of our awning treatment. For this charming result we have built our awning around an adjustable canopy curtain rod, projecting 8″ from the wall and extending for 28″ to 48″ and mounted below a double-draw adjustable traverse rod set projecting a minimum of 4½″. Traverse draperies are then hung on the double traverse rod, sheer draperies on the inner rod and heavy draperies on the outer rod.

Awning is made to shirr onto the canopy curtain rod and extend up to clear the double traverse rod and attach to wall, above window, as illustrated using cut-to-measure rodding inserted in pocket A and attached to wall, above window frame using brackets.

Poles are cut-to-measure 1⅜" fluted cafe rodding with classic or pineapple pole ends. Poles are extended through 1½" buttonhole stitched into awning as illustrated. Pole rests against inside of canopy curtain rod and is attached to wall using a 1¼" wood plug inserted into rod and screwed into the wall.

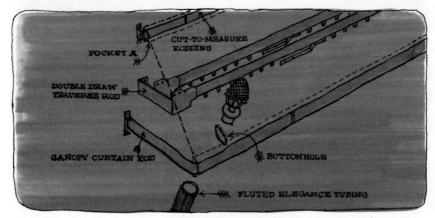

62

Create an ever-changing gallery of your favorite sketches or photos for your wall by mounting them on colorful mats of posterboard and suspending them from either ½" aluminum or ⁹⁄₁₆" decorative cafe rods. Use brass cafe clips to hold the pictures. Or, you can apply this same idea for backing up a daybed or studio couch with a group of small high-fashion decorator pillows. It turns a plain Jane couch into a comfortable conversation piece!

No need to go to a lot of expense when you want a distinctive room divider. Try broad or narrow bands of fabric, match stick, or trim strung taut between two ¾″ to 1⅜″ diameter adjustable cafe rods. These rods have permanently lovely finishes that never need polishing in brass or in antiqued finishes. Rods may be over-painted with standard antiquing kits or household paint without lacquer. If bands of material are wide and of heavy fabric or one continuous panel of match-stick type curtain is used, you need not anchor the bottom rod. Excellent way to separate sleeping and sitting areas in a one-room apartment or to screen off a sewing alcove.

No suction cups to weaken and drop here. No glue or unsightly holes are needed to keep this rod in place. Try the spring tension rod between two cabinets, between almost anything. Available in brass or white, it will hold towels and fill an awkward space usefully and decoratively.

Is there a tired old doorway or archway you want to spruce up a little? The versatile spring tension rod is the key to your solution, holding a softly ruffled valance.

SWAGS AND VALANCES

Plain and pleated or simply sassy, a valance is often the best fashion-right solution for giving an ordinary window an extraordinary elegance of its own. Valances usually project 4½″ to 6½″ from the wall. Where a single two-way draw traverse rod is used, 4½″ of projection is usually adequate. Double-draw traverse rods for under and over traversing draperies, a single-draw traverse rod with a plain rod for traversing draperies and stationary panels, and double plain rods for under and over stationary draperies require projections of 6½″. In rare instances, unusual conditions or construction require greater projections.

The exciting valance ideas illustrated here can be developed using curtain rods for wall installation. You can select adjustable curtain rods in sizes to 120″ with projection up to 8″ on windows up to 48″ wide, up to 6″ projection for windows over 48″. For greater projections on the wider windows, use cut-to-measure oval rodding specially prepared by your dealer.

When you desire a single-draw traverse drapery with valance, select combination traverse and valance rods described on page 29. Bracket and valance kits are available to convert traverse rods to combination traverse and valance.

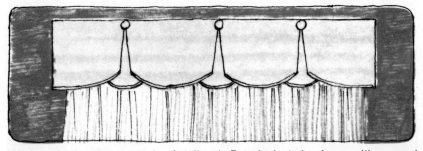

Here's a fresh new approach. A tailored, French-pleated valance with covered buttons, one at the head of each pleat, will go with almost any decor adding a touch of luxury to your window treatment.

64

To create the crisp and frilly effect on the valance, the shirred valance material, hemmed at top and bottom, is slipped onto the valance rod (on top) and the matching single rod on the bottom to form tight, even shirring distributed over the full length of the valance.

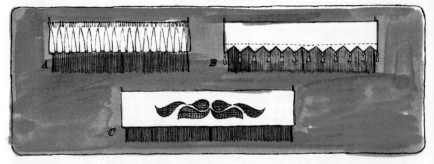

How about these high-fashion valance ideas? A. Loose hanging pleated valance made by eliminating the lower curtain rod. B. Plain valance made of stiff felt stretched across the two rods. C. Using different cut-outs of contrasting felt glued onto the plain valance to add extra interest and color.

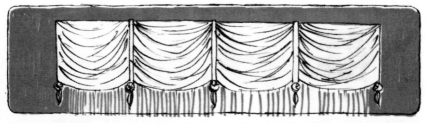

And why not an Austrian valance? A beautiful coordinator for the "return to elegance" look in today's finer homes. It is made just like an Austrian shade with a pocket at the top for shirring it onto the valance rod, use a shirr tape to simplify the preparation.

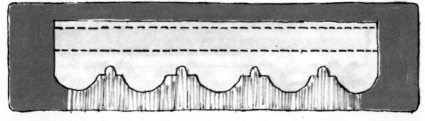

Forever popular and pretty . . . the pinch-pleated valance is easily made using either drapery material or crisp, airy organdy for the criss-cross curtain valance. Particularly effective with early American or country decor.

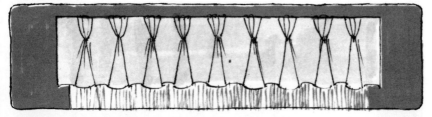

65

Here's a cornice type valance that requires two matching valance rods positioned one above the other as shown (dotted lines). The scalloped valance is fabricated of felt or other stiff fabric cut to any design you may choose and tightly fitted over rods to form a box-like valance. Use over almost any drapery or curtain.

The Swag Drapery . . . pure elegance to the nth degree . . . a high fashion drapery for the tall, massive window found in the larger rooms of today's homes. The swag drapery has luxurious floor-length jabots specially tapered and hung on a cafe rod.

It is made in four pieces and attached over the rod using special swag tape and swag clips. It is often used to frame a window with a conventional drapery treatment. It may also be elegantly used to frame a doorway, a bookcase or even a picture grouping.

The material selected should be fairly heavy and rich in color and weave. Select 1⅜" diameter decorative adjustable cafe rods with distinctive finials, or 1" diameter conventional adjustable cafe rods. For windows over 150" in width, ask your dealer to furnish made-to-measure tubing, either fluted or plain brass.

THREE STEPS FOR MAKING SWAG DRAPERIES

1. Determine the width at the top of the swag, allowing for ½″ side turn-ins and diagonal depth (d-d). Along the diagonal side sew punched shade and swag tape as shown. Make 1½″ casing on top, use ¼″ bottom hem. Use swag clip to pick up loops of punched tape depending on folds desired. Lock clip at top loop. Choose cafe rod or curtain rod to hang swag.

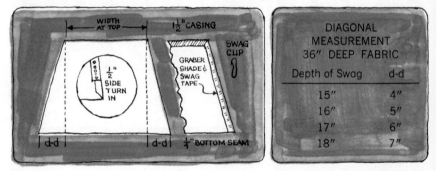

DIAGONAL MEASUREMENT 36″ DEEP FABRIC	
Depth of Swag	d-d
15″	4″
16″	5″
17″	6″
18″	7″

2. Jabots can be any length, short to floor length. Start with a rectangular piece about 25″ wide by desired length. Allow for seaming and finishing of all sides. Cut diagonal on bottom from one corner to a point on the opposite side one-quarter of the length from the bottom. Make three or four pleating folds, allowing for returns, if any. Repeat for the other jabot.

66

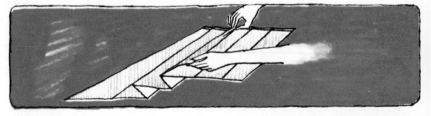

3. Now attach snaps or buttons to folded portion of each jabot and snaps or buttonholes on each end of material to be swagged over full rod between jabots. The sections of your swag drapery treatment are then joined as shown and hung on mounted rod to complete the treatment. You may also hang each section separately using pin-on hooks.

Those wonderful adjustable cafe rods and cut-to-measure cafe rodding are up to some equally wonderful new tricks! There are many unique cornice or valance treatments that can be accomplished using the decorative and conventional types.

Here's a cascading swag with very short jabots to achieve a valance of high fashion elegance.

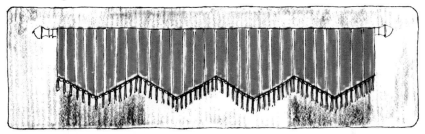

Fringed stripes! . . . a bright and cheerful cafe-valance using stiff striped canvas-type material, felt or corduroy stretched neatly over your brass cafe rod or wood pole so that finials show for a neat, tailored effect.

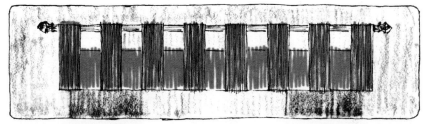

A variation on the stiff cafe-valance is this fresh idea developed on the Roman shade theme with square-cut scallops or alternate colors of stiff fabric sewn together with loose pockets or loops for inserting the rod. The cafe rod is then exposed between loops to add its beauty to the over-all effect. Perfect spot for those fluted rods in any finish.

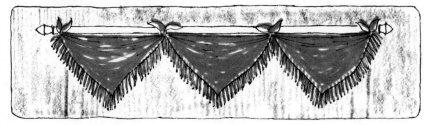

Quick and quaint! Colorful bandanas or triangles of printed or contrasting fabric are knotted casually over a tarnish-resistant cafe rod to give an unusual kitchen, children's room, or den window accent. The same treatment can be modified with pennants for a teen's room, signal flags for an authentic nautical decor.

An interesting and truly unique idea for that decorative cafe-valance. Simply stretch brightly colored felt across two cafe rods or wood poles. The top cafe rod is mounted to the window casing or wall with the lower rod simply inserted in a stitched-in loop hanging free for a scroll effect. You may wish to applique or cut-out and apply an interesting design of contrasting color between the rods. Add some tassels or fringe as you like.

FURTHER COORDINATING RODS WITH DECOR

Today's cafe rods and cafe-traverse rods are carefully designed and finished. These new rods with their finely fluted lines and rich classic and pineapple finials are particularly effective in coordinated schemes. You can select from authentic antiqued finishes which complement contemporary colors so well. Most popular of the finishes offered are: antique brass, antique white (white with gold highlights), black, and some are available in fine woodgrain. One manufacturer offers a decorator white finish, beautiful used as it is, but specially formulated to be over-painted.

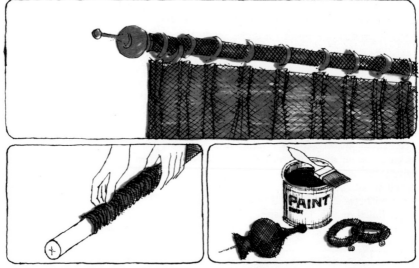

68

Here's an idea for coordinating cut-to-measure wood poles or cut-to-measure brass or aluminum tubing using the same fabric you have used for draperies and furniture as a cover for the poles. To cover the pole, first measure the diameter of the rod and add one inch for the seam. Cut fabric the length of the pole and turn inside out to sew into a tube. Shirr the fabric on the pole and bunch it at one end (see illustration). Then ease it the length of the pole making sure that seam is straight. Next attach the finials, painted to contrast or match, and mount pole above window. Use rings and brackets painted to match.

HELPFUL HINTS ON HEADINGS AND THINGS

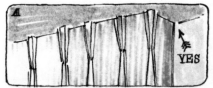

Return those Headings! For that professional finished look to your traverse draperies, be sure to return the last pleat to the wall. Traverse rods generally project one to three inches out from the wall. A drapery pleat should go around the end of the traverse rod (A) or you'll have an unsightly gap.

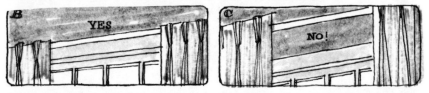

There IS a Correct Height for Traverse Rods. There are times when you may want to make your windows look taller, and there are ways to do it, some of which are in this book (pgs. 27, 45, 78, 84). Avoid placing your traverse rod above the window casing unless you plan to cover it with a decorative cornice or valance. Figure B shows the proper mounting height for a simple traverse rod. Figure C shows how unsightly the rod mounted above the casing is when draperies are opened. Cafe-traverse rods, of course, are an exception.

Correct Position for Drapery Headings. With cafe rods and the newer cafe-traverse rods (drapery hooks are attached to rings or ring slides) the top of the drapery heading should come to the bottom of the rings, so rings are fully visible. With conventional cord or hand draw traverse rods, the top of the drapery heading should be level with the top of the rod. The rod should be concealed when draperies close, yet heading must remain erect.

69

The Proper Length for Draperies . . . Your draperies are the proper length if they reach the window sill, the bottom of the apron, or the floor. Any other length is wrong. If your draperies fall to within 1″ of the floor they will not interfere with baseboard heating efficiency. If your drapery starts below top of window frame, it is then a cafe curtain.

YOUR PROBLEM WINDOWS

70

WHAT IS YOUR WINDOW PROBLEM?

Windows, like people, come all shapes and sizes. Nearly every home has at least one "problem" window, that is, a window or group of windows that seems to defy all efforts to decorate it with a basic window treatment such as those described on pages 13, 14, and 15. If you have such a decorating opportunity, we hope you will find the suitable treatment for it in this section. If none of our solutions fit your problem, write to me, Marie Graber, Middleton, Wisconsin 53562, and I'll do all that I can to find an answer that will turn your problem window into a point-of-pride in your home.

BASIC PROBLEM WINDOW TYPES

1. DOUBLE-HUNG — by far the most common of all window types and therefore involved in more problem situations particularly when it's long and narrow.

2. RANCH OR STRIP — typical in modern ranch homes, this window is usually located high (eye-level) on the wall and rather wide. It may have sliding sashes and is not easily decorated.

3. PICTURE WINDOW — another common window of large expanse usually designed to frame a pleasing outside view with one large, fixed pane of glass which cannot be opened. It may, however, have movable sections on the sides or below the fixed pane.

4. IN-OPENING CASEMENT — opens into your room and presents difficulties with many treatments since draperies tend to become tangled with the window during the opening or closing process.

5. OUT-OPENING CASEMENT — cranked or pushed outward when opened. Not as difficult to decorate as the in-opening casement when a single window. More difficult in pairs or groups.

6. SLIDING GLASS DOORS — increasingly popular in all parts of the country where outdoor living is desired. Often combined for a glass wall effect thus complicating the treatment. Since they must be covered for privacy or light control part of the time, and open for ready access to the patio or lawn this can be a real problem window.

7. WINDOW WALL — a group of picture windows, vertical (floor to ceiling) windows or any expansive window units that combine to form a wall of windows or "glass wall." Difficult to decorate when unit windows of the wall are at various levels, serve different functions, or when bordered by an adjacent door.

8. CORNER WINDOWS — any windows that meet at the corner of a room. Depending on the type of window employed, the corner window is not too difficult to decorate.

9. FRENCH DOORS — usually used in pairs and often open onto a porch or patio or into the room creating a difficult decorating situation.

10. DOUBLE WINDOWS — side by side pairs of windows (if there are more than two they are called multiple windows). They must be treated as a single unit, as one decorating element.

11. BAY WINDOWS — a series of three or more windows set at an angle to each other in a recessed area, bay windows lend themselves to a wide variety of interesting treatments. Even cafe rods can now be used here.

71

12. CATHEDRAL (TRAPAZOIDAL) WINDOWS — slanting windows often found with cathedral ceilings — often an entire wall of the room. Angled or slanting from the top to follow the roof line, this is often a problem area to drape.

13. BOW WINDOW — a circular or curved version of the bay window. Extremely impressive and attractive when properly handled with custom curved rods.

14. AWNING WINDOW — characterized by three or more wide, horizontal sashes that open outward up to 90 degrees from the closed position — often designed with screen or storm window on the inside. Usually this window can be decorated as any standard window.

15. JALOUSIE WINDOW — similar to the awning type window except horizontal panes are narrow strips of glass that open outward by means of a crank. May be decorated as any standard window.

16. DORMER WINDOW — located in an alcove-like extension of a room. Usually a small window. Typical of Cape Cod architecture. Most usually encountered on the second floor. Simple criss-cross curtains or perhaps traverse draperies can be used effectively here.

17. CLERESTORY WINDOW — located near the ceiling, this window is usually rather shallow. Often trapazoidal (slanting) with roof line in contemporary homes, and generally is not decorated at all.

18. ARCHED WINDOW — lovely in its graceful lines, curved at the top and often leaded with many individual panes. This one is a problem, or better stated, a true decorating opportunity, and requires special attention.

72

WINDOWS — TALL, NARROW, HIGH

Even the narrowest, tallest, most poorly proportioned window takes on new high-fashion width, dimension and balance when you use a window-wider traverse rod. This unique rod extends your draperies over the adjacent wall on each side of the window to let in a maximum of light and air. Makes your window appear pleasingly wider. Mounts on window casing, just like any other traverse rod so you will have no holes to mar your walls.

Betray the couturier's art again by making the narrow seem wider. Shirr on cafe curtains using a single adjustable curtain rod. Let the cafe curtains drape to the floor. Full-length over-curtains with valance treatment are hung on a double adjustable curtain rod at the top of the window casing and are tied back at mid-point of window.

TROUBLESOME DOUBLE WINDOWS

If your tall windows come in tandem, treat them as a unit to attain the balancing width, as in this elegant use of cinched and tieback draperies over panel sheers. You can do it all on a double curtain rod, only one set of brackets needed.

Here's an exciting variation of the tandem tall window treatment with variations of its own. You can create the ultimate in high-fashion decor with a pair of 1⅜" decorative cafe or cafe-traverse rods. These distinctive decorator fixtures, in your choice of antiqued finishes, set the mood for luxurious cafe-type draperies. These rods can be used in combination so that under draperies traverse while the over draperies remain stationary or vice-versa! Over draperies can be accented with tassels or fringe. Under draperies hang from ¾ height to floor.

Here's a stunning combination . . . sheer traversing under draperies are framed with heavier contrasting over drapes and a crisp pleated valance to hide those truly troublesome double windows. The key to success with apparent problem windows lies in creating a whole new atmosphere, turning a distracting structural element into a pleasing focal point.

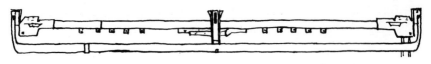

Sugar and spice and everything nice for those hard-to-decorate double windows. Perfect for a cheerful kitchen or a distinctively feminine bedroom using two gleaming brass cafe rods with decorator clips or rings and two tiers of print cafe curtains. Even more sweet with new decorative adjustable cafe rods.

WINDOWS, FAR APART, SEPARATED

75

Be bold! Accent that fireplace or bookshelf that separates two windows. Tie the entire wall together into a stunning focal point with this treatment. Take your traversing over draperies to floor-to-ceiling height with contrasting cafe curtains at the mid-point of the window. Or, for variation, use decorator shades.

Three-quarter cafes offer another interesting solution to the window over a bookcase. Balance your cafes with a frame of wallpaper or decorative grillwork or, perhaps, a drapery swagged to festoon down on either side of the window. The effect is stunning, and the window takes on a new high-fashion dimension.

How much more inviting that sofa or chair grouping appears when balanced by this elegant treatment drawing two separated windows together. To create this treatment, use combination traverse and plain rod, adjustable from 30″ to 180″. Use traverse portion of combination rod to hang your sheer under draperies. Use plain outer rod to hang luxurious outer draperies. The accent here is the combination braided cord and mini-tieback. The unique accessory can be adjusted to allow more full draped effect or to cinch draperies tighter to let in more light. And the cord end detaches simply from the tieback to permit draperies to cover entire window. To complete this treatment, build a decorative cornice of plywood with matching material stapled or tacked to plywood. Finished cornice is attached to wall or casing using L-shaped brackets over entire combination rod.

76

Traverse draperies, long or bookcase length, are a good way to give clean, modern lines to a center fireplace wall as shown. Mount them on a traverse rod attached to wall, or better, to ceiling if you have front-loading rods.

If you have a fine collection of antique glass or something else you want to show to its best advantage, what better way to do it than with glass shelves on either side of the fireplace backed up with soft, stationary draperies on a curtain rod? Select adjustable curtain rods in sizes from 28″ to 120″. For longer lengths, add curtain rod extender or specify cut-to-measure rodding from your dealer.

WINDOWS, HIGH WIDE AND HANDSOME

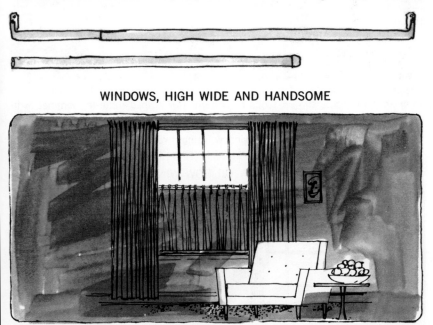

If you don't consider those high ranch-type windows to be particularly blessing, bring them down to earth to mingle with the rest of the room. Try this fashion-able optical illusion accomplished by floor length traverse draperies with inter-mediate length opaque cafes on a decorative adjustable cafe rod. Place cafe brackets on window apron and create a false sill by stopping cafes mid-way to the floor. From every outward appearance, you have a striking double-hung window treatment! And it also allows more variety in furniture arrangement.

A. Draperies are usually sill or apron length on high strip windows and they can be decorated with traverse draperies, cafe curtains or shorty tiers may be shirred onto curtain rods. B. A simple pleated or shirred valance, balanced by a decorative inside window box planter, or even a simple latticework below the window, gives impression of a larger window.

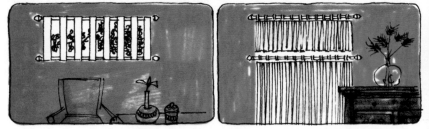

Here are some additional tricks for decorating those high windows: Using any extension cafe rods, slip on strips of patterned or striped material hemmed with a loop at each end. Remember, wide windows need larger diameter rods.

78

Give the impression of a large window using two 1⅜" adjustable cafe rods. Top cafe covers window, bottom cafe on apron with draperies hung to the floor.

CURVED BAY OR BOW WINDOWS

Bay windows are no longer a decorating headache because rods have been specially developed to solve this problem. Ask your dealer for a special order rod. Arrows show how draperies draw smoothly, conforming to curve of bay.

And, if you want a drapery panel at each bend of the window, that's easy, too! Use a one-way adjustable traverse rod on each side and a two-way adjustable traverse rod for the center section. This allows you to close off each frame of the window independently and requires no special order rods.

Here is another lovely treatment of a bay window with a view. Try a traversing drapery on each side of the bay using one-way draw adjustable traverse rods. Finish off the treatment with a valance on pre-bent curtain rodding.

A. One of the loveliest of windows, the curved bow is set off beautifully by a traverse-valance treatment as has been shown on the angular bay. To follow the curve of the window exactly, use a curved traverse rod. B. Try this one, if you like . . . graceful tieback draperies at the side with a brief matching shirred-on cafe curtain on a curved rod to lend privacy and color. Upper rod is curved oval rodding with end draperies shirred onto the rod as stationary panels. Lower rod, also of curved oval rodding, is placed about one-third up from sill.

79

Frame a deep bay in beauty with this easy treatment. Criss-cross curtains on the windows are shirred onto custom-bent rods. Then set it off with heavy draperies on a two-way adjustable traverse and valance rod across the opening.

THOSE CORNER WINDOWS

Here are three solutions to a single problem . . . windows that meet in a corner.

A. Select one-way draw adjustable traverse rods. Draperies open to the extreme ends of the two windows and close to the center (corner) where windows meet for maximum light and ventilation control.

80

B. Select two, two-way draw adjustable traverse rods, to eliminate unsightly corners where wall space between windows and corner shows when draperies are opened and to provide balance to the treatment.

C. To combine the traverse treatment with shirred curtains for added opulence and constant privacy without sacrificing light, select curtain rods with 1½" projection at top, bottom of casing for sheers under traverse draperies.

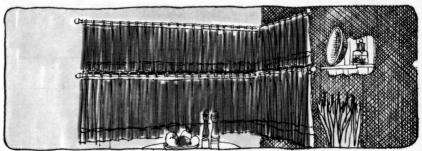

Or, you can tier bright and cheerful cafes on your corner windows, wonderful flexibility plus charm and beauty is yours when you select tarnish-resistant adjustable cafe rod sets in decorative or conventional designs. Join rods at corner using angle connector or butt rods without pole ends.

A touch of luxury for those corner windows can be accomplished with a swag treatment. Floor-length jabots outline draperies with two-toned tassel fringe. In this treatment, jabots take on role of stationary side panels. Sheer under draperies on one-way adjustable traverse rods hang in generous folds, completing the focal point for this bedroom. Swag is custom tailored and festooned over valance rodding or fabricated cornice.

A variation on this theme for the high corner windows combines curtains and valance to achieve a simple, but delightfully different effect. Locked-seam double curtain rods hold shirred-on curtains on inner rod, scalloped valance made from felt or other heavy material on outer rod.

A. If you love the nooks and crannies in Colonial or Cape Cod houses, you probably have more than one dormer window tucked away in your home. Spring tension rods are made for places like these. Holding either ringed cafe curtains or shirred valance and tier curtains, they offer the perfect solution.

B. The old standby, of course, for the dormer window is the light and airy crisscross ruffled curtains shirred onto double curtain rod. Valance rod with 3½" projection is mounted above double curtain rod and holds shirred valance.

CONCEALING AN AIR CONDITIONER

Here's a double traversing or traversing and stationary drapery solution that can make your window treatment as "cool" as the air conditioner makes the room. Double-draw or traverse and plain rod is the answer to the air conditioner that projects too far into the room to be covered any other way. The added projection of the double rod gives the clearance for outer draperies to cover the air conditioner when closed, keep graceful unbroken lines from pleats to hem.

Another now you see it now you don't solution to the air conditioner problem is two tiers of short or long cafes as shown. Upper tier can be open for light and view without disturbing the hiding place of your air conditioner.

Now, if you have your air conditioner in a deep silled window, as shown, you are lucky. Your problem is solved with a shorty drapery and a spring-tension rod set into the window casing. Draw shorty cafes over the unit when not in use.

83

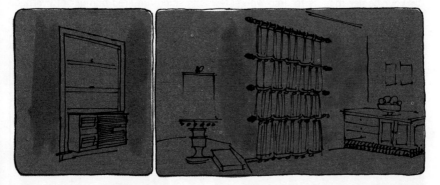

Here is an idea for that window where an air conditioner or fan is located. Four tiers of cafe curtains give charm to the window, privacy to the room . . . and with the bottom two tiers split for hand traversing your problem is solved. Select fluted adjustable cafe rods with cafe clips or rings of proper size to fit rod. Mount as shown and allow for overlap of cafe curtains. Drape to the floor.

ARCHWAYS AND ARCHED WINDOWS

Three solutions to the arched door or window: A. Attractive cafe curtains hung one in front of the other and three quarters high enhance the character of this room.

B. Here, traverse draperies and valance disguise the doorway. This is desirable when the arch is not compatible with the decor of the rest of the room.

C. This high-fashion treatment is really effective when done on a series of windows and archways in a large room. Curved overhead track made-to-measure by your dealer mounts to arch with screws. Position required number of overhead slides and two lockslides for center to attach lead edge of each drapery panel.

One of the most difficult decorating problems . . . uneven windows on a single adjoining wall. Here they are cleverly camouflaged using 4½" projection curtain rods for a distinctive valance in combination with ¾" diameter tarnish-resistant brass finished cafe rods in 28" to 144" extensions mounted at the same height from the floor on each window. Drape frilly edged cafes to the floor — repeat the cafe curtain material on the floor duster tablecloth; your problem is solved, and you have a delightful dining area to enjoy.

A luxurious traditional treatment for the contemporary A-frame windows. Draperies are gracefully tied back and edged with back-to-back rows of gold brocade
fringe. To develop this treatment, select cut-to-measure rodding with lockslides
at peak of slant to hold draperies in place.

Fortunate you are if you have one of those interesting slanting windows found
so often in today's contemporary styled homes. Perhaps the best styling is to
hang ordinary two-way draw draperies on the cross-bar, taking advantage of the
deep overhanging roof to shield the upper section from glaring light. If roof
overhang does not suffice, full-length tapered draperies or a tapered valance can
be hung on a one-way traverse rod or cut-to-measure overhead track to cover the
entire window. Your dealer's help is best put to use on this one.

In many of today's newer homes, particularly where outdoor living is near year-round, window walls are often bordered by a door to a patio. And in many newer duplex two-family (up and down) homes, a picture window is bordered by a door to the porch. It has been difficult to effect a continuous treatment until a unique new combination window and door fixture, called a patio rod, solved the problem. This rod has a conventional two-way cord draw section and a hand traverse section. Traversing draperies cover the window and are operated by cord pulls or cord tension pulley. The same material extends to either right or left covering the door and this section of fabric is opened by a baton when access to the door is desired.

If there is adequate space on both sides of your sliding glass doors, this idea takes advantage of the view. Use a two-way draw adjustable traverse rod extended beyond the door on both sides so that drapery will stack beyond doors.

For a decorator's touch of beauty and distinctive charm, try this cafe treatment for your sliding doors. The cafe-traverse type rod performs like a conventional two-way traverse rod but, because it shows, lends its beauty and distinctiveness to the over-all decor of the room. There are three basic types of cafe-traverse rods offered to allow you the greatest flexibility in coordinating your treatment. Select either 1⅜" adjustable cafe-traverse sets or, for the widest treatments, made-to-measure cafe-traverse rodding.

Among the most ideal windows to decorate are today's lovely picture windows. However, they can be a problem if they have ventilation windows at side or bottom. This solution includes traversing cafe-type draperies on top with conventional cafe curtains which can be located at the mid-point of the window or mounted below the sill to cover ventilation windows beneath the picture window.

Mid-point cafes play tag with swag in this wonderful treatment for the huge picture window. Select adjustable cafe rod of decorative type for swag drapery on top and for cafe curtains at mid-point of window. Coordinate entire effect by adding trimmings to swag and to table lamp!

Wood-grain is still high fashion thanks to the very good simulated wood rods now available. These authentic wood reproductions are fully-adjustable and are made of steel. You'll want to choose either a cafe-traverse rod in 1″ or 1⅜″ diameter, or a cafe-rod in 1⅜″. Matching wood-grain rings hold a waterfall of fabric as the background for any furniture grouping.

GLASS WALLS, TWIN OR TRIPLET WINDOWS

Twin or triplet windows, like twin or triplet people, should be dressed alike for maximum effect. Tie your sets of windows together with stationary panel, a decorative valance or with two-way traverse rod flanked by one-ways as demonstrated in these multiple windows.

Center panel is stationary with the two outside panels traversing to the center panel on one rod. Your dealer will cut-to-measure traverse rodding required for this treatment. All you need to do is give him your window measurements.

One each, one-way left and one-way right adjustable traverse rod and a two-way draw adjustable traverse rod are combined here as indicated (arrows), to accomplish this neat, formally balanced treatment. Flexibility allows you to open or close each of three units separately.

Select two, two-way adjustable traverse rods, one on each side. Valance can be achieved using valance rodding across the entire expanse.

When privacy and light control on your window walls are prime considerations, you'll like this lovely double drapery treatment. Sheer under draperies are either mounted stationary on either an adjustable curtain rod or made-to-measure rodding with over drapery traversing on a two-way adjustable traverse rod or, both draperies traverse on a double-draw adjustable traverse rod set.

If that small window is poorly placed in the room or distracts from the decor you've planned — don't board it up! Blend it with its surroundings by using material to match the wall color or the wallpaper. Hang your cafe type curtains on curtain rod with shirred drapery heading. You may also use the smaller diameter adjustable cafe rods here with a pleated drapery heading.

Here are just a few of the many ways you can handle French doors or casement windows. Perhaps the most effective treatment for French doors is with draw draperies to match the others in the room using swinging door adjustable traverse rods. This unique rod is hinged to allow it to swing open with the doors and works equally well on in-opening casement windows, too, as draperies swing to and fro with the rod as illustrated. The window-wider traverse rod is another good solution, however, it must be mounted above doors and draperies opened before doors can open.

HOME SEWING
WINDOW TREATMENTS WITH
THE CUSTOM LOOK

Instructions prepared by the Department of Sewing Education, The Singer Company, 30 Rockefeller Plaza, New York, N.Y.

TO BUY OR TO MAKE?

Your decision — whether to purchase ready-made or custom-made curtains and draperies or to make them yourself — is based on a variety of personal and budget considerations. Often the ready-mades solve your window decorating needs to a "T," and their wide range of easy-care fabrics today offer attractive and yet practical answers to home upkeep. However, if you do make your own, you can pretty well count on saving a good deal of money and also achieving the added satisfaction of having just what you want in treatment, color, fabric —sometimes impossible to find exactly as you would wish in ready-mades.

Knowledge of various window treatments, how to measure accurately, and construction details are all essential whether you decide to buy or to make. Therefore, in either case the "how to" of making your own draperies and curtains, as suggested here by experts from The Singer Company, will be valuable to you.

In planning your "look," remember to consider not only the inside out, but the outside in. Seek the total effect best suited to the style of your house, type of window, desired lighting, etc. The illustrations in this book depict many different treatments. Any one is easily duplicated or adapted to your particular needs.

The length of draperies and curtains can have a great influence on the total effect desired. Draperies and curtains are made in three desirable lengths, depending on the degree of formality you wish to achieve: to the window sill; to the lower edge of the apron; and to the floor (just clearing the floor or rug). The cafe curtains can be made in many versions: two-tier curtains that come to the sill or lower edge of the apron; one-tier curtains that hang from midway of the upper half of the window to the floor or from the middle of the window to the floor; and three-tier curtains, which usually hang to the sill.

In addition, it is also important to consider the extra touches that will enhance the effect that you are seeking. Headings of various kinds can make a great difference — straight, pleated (Boxed, French, etc.), corded or shirred, scalloped, or a combination of scallop and pleat. You should also think about straight versus tie-back draperies. Or you may wish to try the Austrian shade.

93

MEASURE ACCURATELY FOR CORRECT AMOUNT OF FABRIC

Diagrams (Page 94) show typical windows — Diagram A shows lengths for draperies and curtains and Diagram B shows the number of different versions that are possible for cafe curtains.

The fixture holding the rod in place should be mounted on the extreme ends of the window frame and 1" from the top so that the finished curtains and draperies will cover the entire window frame. It is possible to widen the look of a window by extending rods and draperies beyond the frame, but be sure to decide on this before measuring.

Take window measurements, using a steel tape or folding ruler if possible.

LENGTH. Measure from the top of the rod to the window sill, to the lower edge of the apron, or to the floor.

WIDTH. Measure from edge to edge of the window frame. To this width, add the depth of the return at each end. (The measurement for the return will be used again for positioning the end pleat in the drapery heading.)

These are basic window measurements. To them you must add allowances for fullness, heading, casing, and hems. The width of the hem and the fullness may vary with the individual; however, the amounts shown below are acceptable.

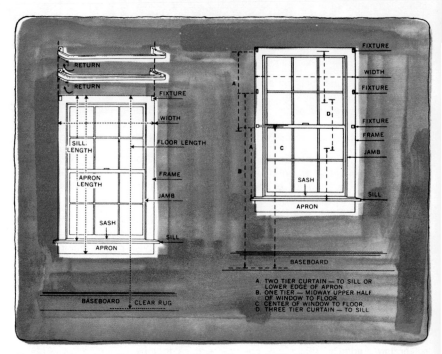

Labels in the image:

RETURN
RETURN
FIXTURE
WIDTH
SILL LENGTH
FLOOR LENGTH
APRON LENGTH
FRAME
JAMB
SASH
APRON
SILL
BASEBOARD — CLEAR RUG

FIXTURE
WIDTH
FIXTURE
FIXTURE
FRAME
JAMB
SASH
SILL
APRON
BASEBOARD

A TWO TIER CURTAIN — TO SILL OR LOWER EDGE OF APRON
B. ONE TIER — MIDWAY UPPER HALF OF WINDOW TO FLOOR.
C CENTER OF WINDOW TO FLOOR.
D THREE TIER CURTAIN — TO SILL

For glass curtains: To the measured length add 8½" (2" for double heading, 1" for casing, ¼" for turning, and 2" for shrinkage tuck plus 3¼" for bottom hem and turning). If double bottom hems are used, and they are desirable in sheer fabric, allow 6" for the bottom hem instead of 3¼".

Multiply the measured width by 2½ or 3 for fullness. To this figure add 8" for hems (1" double hems on each side of the two panels).

Based on this system of measuring, let us take a typical example and determine the correct amount of fabric to buy. If the width of your rod (including returns) is 60", you will need at least three times that plus 8" (for hems) in fabric width. Since fabrics come in varying widths, be sure to allow enough — for example, with a 48" wide fabric you should buy four widths (or a total of 192"). Sometimes the width may be a bit more than you need, but it is better to have the extra fullness than to have skimpy curtains. Now, to determine the total amount of fabric needed, multiply the number of necessary widths — in this case 4 — by the desired length — say, 84" including hem allowances. This will give you the yardage required — 336" or 9⅓ yards per window. It is advisable to buy an extra 9" to allow for straightening the ends of the fabric.

For lined draperies: To the measured length (as described on previous page), add 8½" (1" for heading, 4" for top hem plus 3½" for bottom hem and turning).

For unlined draperies: Add an additional ½" for turning on the top hem.

Determine the width of your finished draperies after pleating the heading. To this width add the depth of the return at one end plus 3" for hems (1" hem and ½" seam allowance on each side), plus the amount required for pleats.

Pleats look best in the opinion of the experts when made in an uneven number. Each side of the drapery should have at least 5 pleats, and wider ones 5 or 9 pleats on each side. Allow 5" or 6" for fullness, space them about 4" apart.

One end pleat is always located just the depth of the return from the outside edge of each panel; and the other end pleat 2" from the inside edge; the distance between these two pleats is used to figure the space between additional pleats. Since two end pleats are predetermined in each panel, the number of spaces is always one less than the number of pleats. If you plan on 5 pleats, divide the distance between the end pleats by four to determine the space between the pleats.

Most drapery fabrics are 50" or 60" wide, and generally two widths are sufficient for a pair of draperies. Let's take a typical example and determine the correct amount of fabric to buy. If the desired length is 97" including allowances for hem and heading, multiply this length by 2 widths. This will give you the yardage required — 194" or 5 yards and 14 inches per window. Buy an additional 9" to allow for straightening the ends of the fabric.

If fabric with a design is selected, the design must fall in the same place in each panel; therefore, extra yardage is required for matching. A full design should begin at the turn for the bottom hem. Measure from the center of one design to the center of the next one and allow this amount in each panel length for matching.

The lining is cut 10" shorter and 4" narrower than the drapery fabric.

DRAW DRAPERIES require greater width, because they cover the entire window when drawn to the center. Measure length the same as instructed for lined draperies.

For width, measure across the window from one end of the rod to the other. To this measurement, add the depth of the return on each side. Use this measurement to determine the number of pleats and the space between the pleats.

Pleats in draw draperies must always be even in number; however, there may be an even or uneven number of pleats in each panel. Allow 5" to 6" for fullness in each pleat, and space pleats about 4" apart.

An end pleat is always located the depth of the return from the outside edge of each drapery panel, and the distance between these two pleats is used to figure the space between additional pleats. Since two pleats are predetermined, the number of spaces is one less than the number of pleats. It may be necessary to estimate the number of pleats several times before determining the exact number and the exact spacing. For 24 pleats divide the distance between the end pleats by 23 to determine the space between the pleats. For fullness, multiply the number of pleats by the fullness of a pleat.

To the width of the window and depth of the return at each end, add 6" for hems (1" hem and ½" seam allowance on each side of the two panels) plus 2½" for the overlap plus the amount required for pleats and seam allowances within the drapery. Each finished panel must be one-half this width.

FOR CAFE CURTAINS. Decide on the type of rod, hooks, and style of heading for your cafes before taking the measurements. A rod is required for each curtain tier. Diagram B on page 94 shows the positions of the rods for several styles.

LENGTH. Measure from the lower circle of the ring to the top of the next rod, or to the sill, or to the floor. To this measurement, add the allowances for the top and bottom hems. (The bottom hem is usually 3" plus ½" for turning. The heading hem may be 3" or 4" plus ½" for turning, depending on the style).

WIDTH. Measure from the inside edge of one bracket to the other. Multiply this measurement by 2 for fullness. To this figure add 6" for hems (1" hem and ½" for turning on each side of the two panels). If you plan on a pleated heading, make the allowance for the pleats instead of the double fullness.

HOW TO MAKE BASIC CURTAINS AND DRAPERIES

A WORD ABOUT NEEDLE AND THREAD AND MACHINE STITCH LENGTH

Thread should be as close in color and weight as the fabric you are sewing. Choose silk thread for silk and/or mercerized thread for cottons, linens and some blends. Synthetic fabrics should be stitched with silk, synthetic or mercerized thread. A size 14 needle is best for mercerized thread; size 11 for fine synthetic threads. For sheer fabrics, select a 12 to 15 stitch length on your sewing machine and loosen the tension slightly if synthetic or silk thread is used. For medium-weight fabrics, select a 10 to 12 stitch length.

Curtains. Glass curtains are curtains of sheer fabric that hang straight from the rod against the glass to the sill or floor and are used alone or under draperies and other curtains such as criss-cross curtains. Basically, all curtains are made the same. They are made with plain headings and casings at the tops, and hung on a single rod when used under draperies, or they may be made with pleated or shirred headings when used alone.

Double-fold hems are desirable in sheer fabric since they eliminate the turned raw edge that would normally show through. In the measurements on page 94 5¼" were added for the casing, heading, and shrinkage tuck at the top; and 6" for a double-fold hem at the bottom. With sheer fabric, allow three times the window width for attractive fullness, and add 8" for a 1" double-fold hem on the side and center hems so panels can be interchanged. (See Diagrams A-B-C.)

First, finish the side hems. Turn a scant 1" to the underside and pin in place. Press the fold. Make the second 1" turn and pin, then press the fold. Stitch close to the fold. Press.

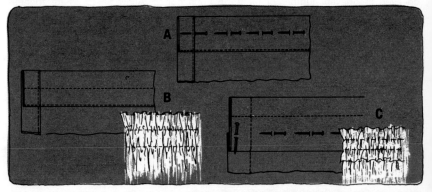

For the casing and heading, turn ¼" to the underside and press. Then turn 2" to the underside and pin the free edge in place. Press along the top fold. Stitch close to the first fold. Press along the top fold. Stitch close to the first fold. Reinforce with backstitching. Press. Divide the hem for the casing and heading by placing a row of pins midway between the stitching and top edge. Stitch along this line; backstitch at each end.

To make shrinkage tuck, measure 1" below the stitching line on the right side of the fabric. Pin a 1" tuck in place and stitch, following the same line of stitching used in making the top hem. This tuck will also make a smart heading, and, if the curtains should shrink the tuck can be let out.

Before turning the bottom hem, compare the two panels to be sure they are the same length. Place them wrong sides together, and check the length at the center and outside hems.

Then, turn under a scant 3" and pin along the fold. Make a second 3" turn and pin the first fold to the curtain. Before pressing the hem, hang the curtains on the rod. Adjust the fullness and check the length. If there is a slight difference in the length, adjust the hem width accordingly. Press the hem and stitch it in place close to the fold. Backstitch at each end.

Weight the bottom hems so that the curtains will hang evenly. A round-bead weighted tape is most suitable. Draw the weighted tape through the hem in back of the double turn and secure it on the underside with diagonal hand stitches.

Unlined Draperies. If you like the informal approach to decorating, unlined draperies of light or medium-weight fabric should be your choice. These may be finished with a shirred or pleated heading. (See "Headings," page 102.)

When cutting drapery lengths be sure to start with a true crosswise grain. Do not tear the fabric. Snip the selvage and pull a thread on the crosswise to indicate the cutting line, then cut along the drawn thread.

In the measurements on page 94, 4½" were allowed for the heading hem and turning. Unless you choose a commercial pleater tape for your heading (this is discussed later) you must apply stiffening to the drapery to support the heading. For this, cut strips of 4" crinoline, 3" shorter than the width of each drapery panel. Pin the crinoline to underside of the drapery heading ½" from the top edge and 1½" in from either side of the fabric. (This is the turn for the side hems.) Stitch together ¼" from the lower edge of the crinoline. Next, turn the top edge of the drapery fabric over the top edge of the crinoline ½" and stitch. Press. Turn the heading hem to underside along the edge of crinoline. Pin and baste hem in place. Do not stitch the hem; when the pleats are stitched, they will hold the hem in place. (Remove this basting after the pleats are stitched.)

Side hems may be slip-stitched by hand or machine-stitched, using either straight stitching or blindstitching. To remove bulk, cut out the corners of the top hem edges. Begin 1½" from the outer edge (turn for side hem) and cut upward to within ½" of the top fold; then cut diagonally to the hem fold, and on the hem fold to the outer edge. Then turn the side hem edge to the underside ½"; press. Then turn a 1" hem; pin. Miter the corners at the top edge. Diagrams A: Stitch stiffening to top of drapery. B: Finish side hem by hand, using slip-stitch. C: Finishing double side hems and bottom hem by hand. D: Blindstitch hemming.

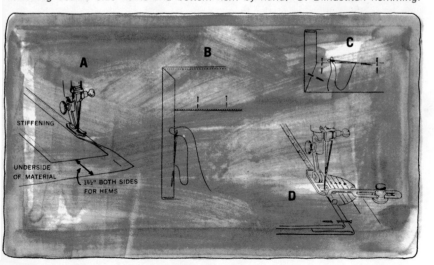

If the hem is finished by hand, catch only a few threads of the fabric in the stitches so they will be invisible on the top side. If it is machine stitched, using straight stitching, place the stitching close to the folded edge. If the hem is blindstitched, baste the hem in place ¼" from the folded edge. With the wrong side up turn the hem under to the right side, creating a soft fold and exposing the ¼" edge. Stitch, using the blindstitch zig-zag.

Hem the bottom of the draperies, following the instructions for "Lined Draperies," page 100. However, sew the hem in place as instructed above.

MAKING DRAPERIES WITH PLEATER TAPE HEADING

Conventional pleater tape with woven-in pockets for pleater pins or the new perfect pleat method for pinch-pleats can be used instead of 4" crinoline in the heading hem. These ready-made pleat tapes are fashioned to give approximately double fullness and the pleats are premeasured.

Refer to the instructions for measuring on page 94. Eliminate the 4" allowance for the top hem; however, allow ½" for turning.

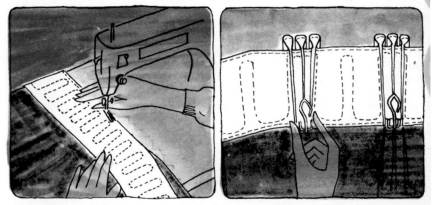

The perfect pleat method was used in the instructions that follow; however, use these instructions for pleater tape up to the point of forming the pleats. Pleating areas are precreased; space areas between pleats are not. The printed stitching line is on the right side of the tape.

Consider the return at each end of the drapery and position the tape so that one end pleat falls at the turn of the rod and the other end pleat falls about 2" from the center edge. Cut the tape 3" shorter than the width of each drapery panel. Remember to make one panel for the right side of the window and the other for the left.

Pin the tape over the top of the drapery, wrong sides together, ⁵⁄₁₆" from the fabric edge; extend the ends to within 1½" of the drapery edge (turn for side hems). Stitch the tape in place ½" from the fabric edge. Press. Turn the tape to the underside, fold the fabric on the stitching line, and press. Pin the lower edge of the tape to the fabric and stitch ¼" from the tape edge. Press.

Finish the side and bottom hems as instructed above.

To form the pleats. If perfect pleat is used, form each pleat at the precreased points. Pinch the pleats and insert the special clip into the clip slots of the tape, following the instructions furnished in the pleat tape kit. The hook provided with the clip should be inserted at the point that provides the proper heading for the type of rod you used.

If pleater tape is used, insert pleater hooks into the pockets to form the pleats.

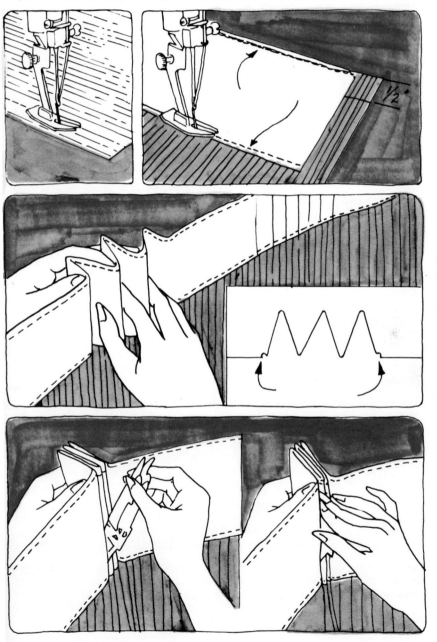

LINED DRAPERIES

More formal draperies are usually lined as are those that need extra weight to hang well. Linings should be cut to allow for a 2" hem at the bottom and a ½" seam allowance across the top and sides. See Diagram A for the proportion of lining to the drapery fabric panel. (This is based on a drapery with a 4" hem at the top, 1" side and 3" bottom hems.)

For the heading, cut a strip of 4" crinoline 3" shorter than the width of the drapery panel. Pin the crinoline to the underside of the drapery heading with the top edges even and 1½" from either side of the drapery fabric. (Turn for side hems.) Stitch ¼" from the fold for the hem. Press. (A, B, C, D, page 97; Diagrams A thru F, page 101.)

For the side hems, turn 1½" to the underside and press.

Hem the lower edge of the lining. Turn under ½" and fingerpress. Turn a 2" hem to the underside and pin in place. Stitch close to the fold. Press.

At the top of the lining, turn under a ½" seam allowance and press. Next pin the lining to the drapery side hems, right sides together, with the top fold of the lining 7½" below the top of the drapery fabric and the bottom hem 5½" above the lower edge. Stitch, from the lining side, taking a ½" seam. Press, clip into the seam allowances at 3" or 4" intervals. Then press the seam edges toward the lining. Turn the drapery right side out and adjust the hem on each side. Press.

Turn the heading hem to the underside and press. Cut out the corners of the top hem edge. Begin 1½" from the outer edge (turn of side hem) and cut upward to within ½" of the top fold; then cut diagonally to the hem fold, and on the hem fold to the outer edge. Then turn the side hem edge under ½"; turn the 1" hem over the heading hem and pin. Miter the corners at the top.

Lap the top edge of the lining over the edge of the heading hem ½" and pin. Slip-stitch the mitered corners and lining in place, making the stitches through the hems and lining only.

100 Hem the bottom of the drapery. First, compare the two panels, wrong sides together, and check the length at center and outside hems to be sure they are identical. Then turn the edge under ½" and stitch close to the fold. Press. Turn a 3" hem to the underside and pin it in place. Miter the corners so they will fit smoothly under the lining. Ease the hem down slightly at this point to allow for the thicknesses of fabric and to square the corners. Sew weights to each side seam allowance to prevent them from drawing.

Before you finish the hem, pleat the heading and attach the drapery hooks as instructed on pages 98 and 102. Hang the draperies and check the length. Let the draperies hang for two or three days because many fabrics will shrink or stretch. If there is a slight difference in length, adjust the hem width accordingly.

The bottom hem can be finished after the draperies are hung. Slip-stitch the hem and mitered corners in place. Catch only one or two threads in the drapery fabric and make the stitches through the hems only at the mitered corners. Do not press this hem. If it is necessary to lengthen the draperies slightly after six months or so, there will be no crease to mar the fabric.

The lining hangs free of the drapery. To hold it in position, use French tacks spaced about 12" apart.

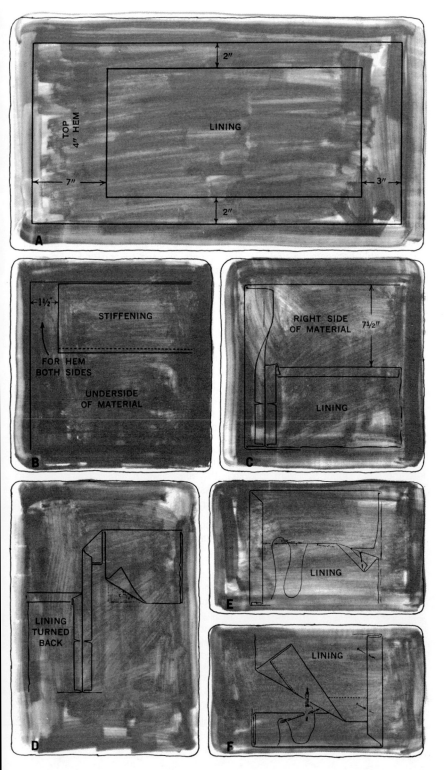

A

2"

TOP
4" HEM

LINING

7"

3"

2"

B

1½"

STIFFENING

FOR HEM
BOTH SIDES

UNDERSIDE
OF MATERIAL

C

RIGHT SIDE
OF MATERIAL

7½"

LINING

D

LINING
TURNED
BACK

E

LINING

F

LINING

MAKING HEADINGS FOR DRAPERIES AND CURTAINS

There are a number of ways you can finish the headings on the draperies you make. These are detailed here for you. The same headings may be used on curtains, too.

PLEATS IN PANEL DRAPERIES. Panel draperies should have an uneven number of pleats in each panel; draw draperies may have an even or uneven number in each panel, resulting in an even number in each pair. The decision on the number of pleats, the allowance in each pleat, and spacing between pleats should be made before cutting the fabric for the draperies. See pages 94 and 95.

Always measure and pin-mark position of pleats and spacing before stitching.

For panel draperies, measure 2" from the center edge of the drapery and pin-mark. Then measure and pin-mark the width of the first end pleat. At the opposite edge, measure and pin-mark the depth of the return. Then measure and pin-mark the width of the second end pleat. Place the third pleat at the exact center between the first and second end pleats. Space the remaining pleats evenly between the first and third pleats and the second and third pleats. (See Diagram A.) Compare the two panels, wrong sides together, to be sure the pin-marks correspond.

PLEATS IN DRAW DRAPERIES. For draw draperies, there is a 2½" overlap when a two-way traverse rod is used; therefore, the first end pleat must be farther from the center edge than in panel draperies. Using the measurements in the example on page 94, measure 3¼" from the center edge of the drapery and pin-mark. Then measure and pin-mark the width of the first end pleat. At the opposite end, measure and pin-mark the width of the return. Then measure and pin-mark the width of the second end pleat. Continue measuring and marking the space, then the width of the pleat. The spaces between the last and first pleats must be the same, and the width of all pleats must be the same. Compare the two panels, wrong sides together, to be sure the pin-marks correspond.

To form pleats, fold through the center of the space marked for each pleat and pin. Stitch from the edge to ½" below the heading hem, placing the stitching into the pleat about ⅛6" from the pins (this allows width, which the thicknesses of the layers of fabric will take up). Backstitch at each end for reinforcement. These steps are the same for all types of pleats. (See Diagram B.)

BOX PLEATS are large pleats pressed flat so that the folds are an equal distance from center line of the pleat. For best results, try to figure box pleats uniformly, with the space between each pleat the same width as the finished pleat.

PINCH PLEATS are made by dividing the large pleats you have formed into three smaller pleats. Form these pleats, then press the length of the pleat. At the lower edge, either hand-tack the three pleats together or machine stitch across them just below the stiffened heading. If you hand-tack them the shank of the drapery hook can be inserted into the pleat. Pinch pleats are very attractive in firm, crisp fabrics that take pleats with a clean edge. (See Diagram C.)

CARTRIDGE PLEATS are round 2" to 2½" pleats that are left loose at the lower end and filled with cotton, kapok, rolls of stiff paper, buckram, or pellon, which holds the cartridge shape. They should be spaced about 2" to 3" apart. (See Diagram D, E.) Cartridge pleats are frequently placed in groups of three.

FRENCH PLEATS are large pleats divided into three small pleats like pinch pleats but not creased. Form the three pleats at the lower edge of the heading. Then

hand-sew through the pleats several times before drawing tightly on the threads.
Tie the threads on the underside. (See Diagram F.)

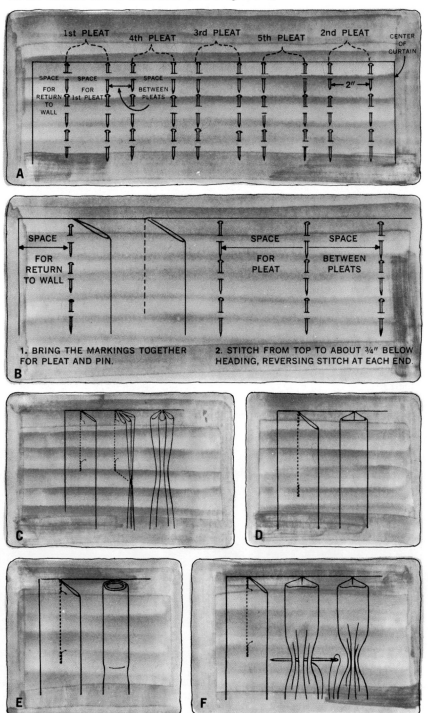

A

1st PLEAT   4th PLEAT   3rd PLEAT   5th PLEAT   2nd PLEAT   CENTER OF CURTAIN

SPACE   SPACE   SPACE BETWEEN PLEATS
FOR RETURN TO WALL   FOR 1st PLEAT
2″

B

SPACE FOR RETURN TO WALL   SPACE FOR PLEAT   SPACE BETWEEN PLEATS

1. BRING THE MARKINGS TOGETHER FOR PLEAT AND PIN.

2. STITCH FROM TOP TO ABOUT ¾″ BELOW HEADING, REVERSING STITCH AT EACH END.

C

D

E

F

103

CORDED OR SHIRRED CURTAIN HEADINGS. This is a very attractive treatment for finishing the heading of sheer or other lightweight curtains. The number of rows of shirring you make depends on the width of the heading itself. Shirred curtains should always be made full — 2½ or 3 times the width of the window.

Make the side and bottom hems as outlined in the general construction details. Make the top hem as deep as it should be to accommodate as many rows of shirring as you plan. Turn the top edge under ¼" and press. Then turn the hem to the underside and press. Stitch.

Measure and pin-mark the stitching lines for the corded shirring, starting ¾" below the top edge and spacing the lines ¾" apart; and allow ¼" below the lines for the cord. Insert a length of cable cord (⅛" or ³⁄₁₆" in diameter) between the two layers of fabric and close to the previous stitching. Stitch close to the cord from the inside edge of one side hem to the other, using the zipper foot on your machine. Repeat the procedure for each row of cording. You will then have a heading hem with several rows of cord stitched into crosswise casings. Pull the threads to the underside and tie them. Fasten the cords at one end by turning under ¼" and making several hand stitches through the cord and underside of the curtain.

Pull on the cords and at the same time, ease the fabric back on the cords to form uniform gathers. When you have shirred the curtain for the correct width, fasten the loose cord ends as you did the opposite end. (See Diagrams A, B, C.)

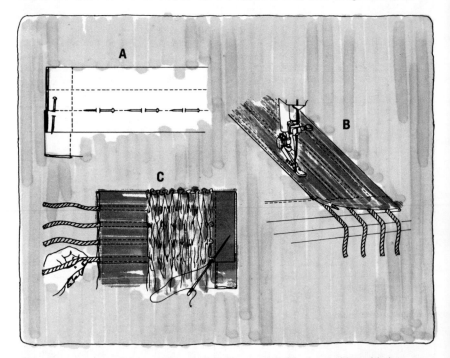

There are commercial woven-in cording tapes available for making shirring easy. When using this type of tape allow for a ¾" turn under at the top of the curtain. Place tape on the underside of the curtain and stitch above the top and bottom cords in the woven-in tape. Then stitch on one side of each cord between top and bottom of the next cord. Knot the cords at one end and draw from other end to adjust shirring fullness. Anchor the cords at end.

SCALLOPED HEADINGS may be used on draperies and cafe curtains. A stiffening of crinoline is used to support the heading. In cutting a curtain length, allow 4½" for the top hem.

Scallops may be made almost any width desired, but they should be even in number. Some of the latest sewing machines come with a circular-stitch accessory that enables you to make perfect scallops 2" to 10" across, also controlling proportional scallop depth. Plan on six, eight, or ten scallops per curtain width. (Diagrams A, B, C will show you the basic steps in scalloping.)

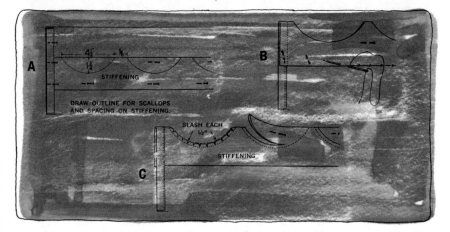

Cut a strip of 4" crinoline as long as the width of the curtain minus side hem allowances. Draw an outline for the scallops and the space between scallops on the crinoline, as illustrated. Turn and press the side hems. Pin the crinoline to the wrong side of the curtain 4¼" below the top, and extend the ends to the turn for the side hems. Slip the ends of the crinoline under the side hems and stitch the hems. Turn the top; hem to the right side along the edge of the crinoline and pin. Stitch the scallops, using a shorter stitch than that used in stitching the fabric. Press.

105

Cut away the crinoline close to the stitching. Cut out the scallops ¼" from the stitching. Clip into the seam allowances at ½" intervals. Turn the hem to the wrong side, over the crinoline and turn the scallops smoothly on the stitching line and press. Turn the edge of the top hem under ¼" and press. Pin, then stitch the hem to the body of the curtain.

If you wish, scallops may be combined with loops through which the rods are slipped. For these, add 3½" for the length of the loops, plus 7¼" at the top for the facing hem. Cut a strip of crinoline 7" wide and the length of the width of your curtain minus side hem allowances. Draw outline for scallops and loops on the crinoline. Loops may be straight or pointed. Stitch, and finish the seam as described for the scalloped heading above. Adjust the curtain length on rod by turning the loops to underside. When you have determined how much to turn back, stitch across the end of the loop. If you want to use button-on loops, turn the loops to the right side and make buttonholes in the loops and sew buttons on the curtain. (See Diagram D — page 106.)

SCALLOPS WITH FRENCH PLEATS. If you want to combine scallops with French pleats, allow 4¼" for the heading hem and 3½" for the bottom hem. Draw an outline of the scallops on the crinoline with wider spacing allowed for the pleats. If you are using fabric 48" wide for each panel, allow 3" for side hems (1" hem and ½" for turning on each side), 3" for the return at the outside edges, 4" for each scallop, and 4¾" for each pleat. You can make 5 French pleats and 4 scallops. (See Diagram E.)

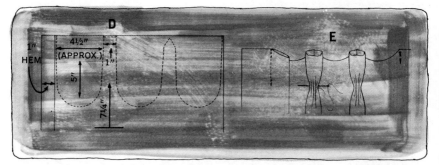

Follow the same construction procedure as for scalloped headings except for the top hem finish. Turn the hem under ¼" and stitch separately. At the points between scallops make French pleats as described previously in the instructions for French pleats.

Pointed headings are made like scallops except that points are made instead of scallops.

Commercial scallop tapes measuring 3" wide are available, and may be used to make scalloped and pleated headings. The tape is placed on the right side of the fabric along the top edge. The tape is then stitched to the fabric ¼" from top edge. Scallops are cut out close to edge of tape, and then the tape is turned to underside of the fabric and pressed in place. The lower edge of the tape is stitched to the curtain. Pleats are formed by inserting pleater pins into the woven-in pockets of the tape.

HANGING DRAPERIES

Selecting the best hook to achieve the desired results is very important. The wrong hook or hooks improperly used can spoil the effect and make even the most elaborate treatment look bad. You will find generally, that the type of heading and the hanging method determine the type of hook you will use.

Essentially there are four types of hooks from which to choose:

1. The Pleater Hook is used with pleater tape headings and is designed with separate prongs to fit into tape to form and hold the pleat folds.

2. The Over-rod Hook is designed to fit over curtain rodding and is most often used for stationary draperies.

3. The Adjustable Hook may be used over the rod or attaches to traverse slides and adjusts up or down to allow you the greatest possible flexibility in application.

4. Most often, Standard-type Hooks are designed to hook into traverse slides.

HOW TO ADD THOSE EXTRA TOUCHES

Ruffles are used on a variety of curtain types. You will see them on criss-cross tiebacks and on straight hanging curtains ruffled all around, and on valances. Ruffles are usually cut on the crosswise grain of the fabric. However, when yards and yards of ruffling are required, it is best to cut lengthwise strips. Ruffles cut on the lengthwise grain will remain fluffy longer, and need fewer joining seams.

Ruffles may be as narrow as 3″ or as wide as 8″. Double or triple fullness may be required. The fullness is governed by the width of the ruffle as well as the texture of the fabric. Wide ruffles require more fullness than narrow ones. And sheer fabrics require greater fullness than heavier fabrics.

First join your ruffle strips with a very narrow French seam or use the hemmer foot on your machine. Before you gather the ruffle, hem the edge with the hemmer foot. Hem both edges if the ruffle has a heading.

Use the ruffler on your machine for even gathers. Adjust the setting of the ruffler and test the fullness of the ruffle on a swatch of your fabric. (See Diagrams A, B, C, D.)

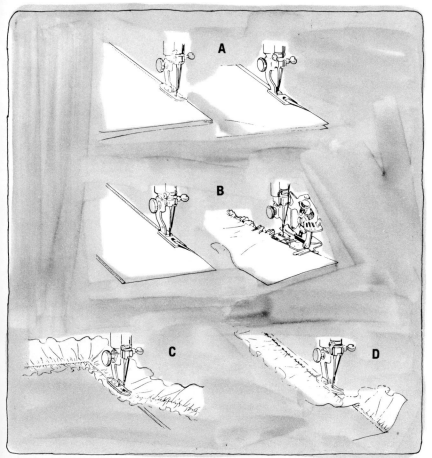

107

Joining ruffling with a heading to the curtain is done after first finishing center and lower edges of curtains with a very narrow hem, using the hemmer foot. Pin the ruffle to the hemmed curtain edge with right sides up and stitch through the ruffle stitching row. Ease in fullness at the corners. This type of joining leaves a little ruffled "heading" sticking up above the joining.

To join a ruffle without this little heading, pin the ruffle to the curtain wrong sides together. Seam together. Trim seams to a scant ¼″ and press seam up toward curtain. Turn curtain over the seam bringing right sides of the curtain and ruffle together and stitch through first row of stitching.

Ruffles applied as valances are pinned and stitched to the top matching rows of stitching. Ruffled valance edges are finished with a narrow hem.

TIEBACKS. Tiebacks may be shaped or straight. To estimate the length of the tieback, loop a strip of material around the hung drapery or curtain, drawing to the side of the window for best effect.

Shaped tiebacks are usually interlined with heavy material or crinoline and lined or faced. Cut a paper pattern 3″ to 4″ wide at the center, tapering to 2″ or 2½″ at the ends. Cut the fabric, lining and crinoline by this pattern, allowing ⅜″ seams on all edges. Pin the crinoline to underside of fabric and the lining to the right side. Stitch together leaving an opening of 3″ or 4″ for turning. (See Diagrams A, B.)

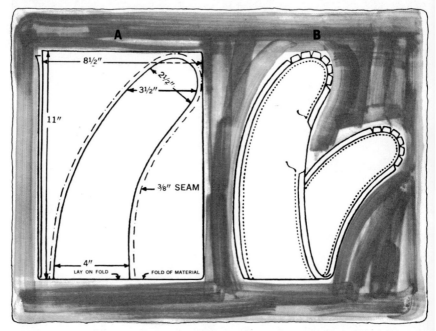

Trim the crinoline seam allowance close to the stitching line and the lining seam allowance to a scant ¼″. Press. Turn to the right side, fold on the stitching line and press. Slip-stitch the opening. Sew small bone rings or very narrow fabric loops at ends of bands.

Straight tiebacks with one ruffle are used with ruffled tieback curtains. Cut the band on the lengthwise grain the required length and 2½″ wide. Crease through the center, wrong sides together. Make the ruffle the same width as the curtain ruffle and the same length as the band; finish each end of the ruffle with a ⅛″ hem. Pin the wrong side of the ruffle to the right side of the band, extending the ends of the band ¼″ beyond the ruffle. Stitch. Press the seam allowances toward the band. Turn under ¼″ on the free side of the band and press. Turn the band, right sides together, and stitch across each end, taking a ¼″ seam. Press, and cut diagonally across the corners. Turn the band to the right side and pin the folded edge in place at the stitching line, enclosing the seam allowances inside the band. Top-stitch close to the fold. Press.

AUSTRIAN SHADE

This elegant shade generally is made of sheer or semi-sheer fabric and the bottom edge is finished with fringe. An Austrian Shade is easy to make when you use shirring tape. This tape has woven-in cords for shirring the shade and plastic rings through which cord is laced so that the shade can be raised.

A. Rod for hanging shade is drawn through top hem or casing. B. Rigid rod drawn through loops or rings at lower end of tape holds shade evenly. C. Braided cord is drawn through rings of tape from the bottom up and across to one side at the top for raising and lowering shade.

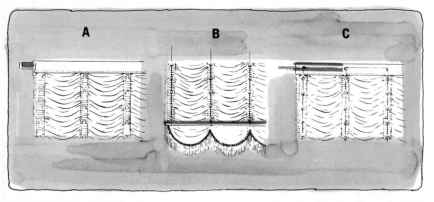

CUTTING THE FABRIC. Measure the window to determine the length and width of the finished shade. Cut the fabric 3 times the finished length, plus 1" for the bottom hem; and the finished width, plus 3" for 1½" hem on each side, plus 3" in each shirred section to create the scalloped effect when the top of the shade is gathered. (The scallops are usually about 12" wide.)

For the top casing cut a strip of fabric on the lengthwise grain and the length of the finished shade, plus 2" for hems, and 5" wide.

FINISHING THE BOTTOM EDGE. At the bottom edge, turn a scant ½" to the right side and press. Then turn a ½" hem to the right side and press. On the right side of the fabric, pin fringe over the hem with the fringe barely above the top fold for the hem. Stitch the fringe and hem in place; reinforce with backstitching. Stitch a second time ¼" below the first stitching.

109

SIDE HEMS. Along each side of the shade, turn the edge under ½" and press. Turn under a 1" hem and press. Stitch, then press again.

THE SHIRRING TAPE METHOD. Cut length of the shirring tape 1" longer than the fabric for the shade. You will need one length more than the number of scallops. Begin each tape with the plastic rings in the same position.

On the wrong side of the fabric, pin a strip of tape 1" from the outside edge and 1" below the top edge. Stitch on each side of the tape from the top edge of the tape to within 1" of the fringe on the shade. Backstitch at each end. Stitch a strip of tape to the opposite side in the same manner.

Mark the position for the scallops at even intervals between the outside tapes. Pin a strip of tape over the markings and stitch in place.

At each end of the shirring tape, knot the ends of the cords so they will not slip out of the tape. At the bottom of the shade, turn up the end of the excess tape ¼", then turn up the tape and stitch the end in place to form loops for the rod.

FINISHING THE TOP EDGE. Hem each end of the strip for the casing with a ½″ double-fold hem.

The shade fabric is wider than the length of the casing because 3″ were allowed in each scallop for fullness. At the top edge, form a small pleat (1½″) on each side of the scallop close to the shirring tape.

Pin the casing strip to the top edge of the shade right sides together, with the outer edges of the shade and casing strip even. Adjust the small pleats, if necessary. Stitch, taking a ½″ seam; backstitch at each end.

Press, then press both seam allowances toward the casing strip. Turn under the free edge of the strip ½″ and press. Turn the casing strip to the underside and pin in place at the stitching line, enclosing the seam allowance. Stitch; backstitch at each end. Press.

TO GATHER THE SHADE. At the top edge of the shade, pull the woven-in cords of the tape and gather the shade for the desired length. Be sure the gathers are even; that the length is the same at each strip of tape, and that the rings on the shirring tape are even horizontally. Cut off the cords about 3″ from the tape, knot the ends together and sew them to the shade.

HANGING THE SHADE. Cut around rod 1″ shorter than the width of the shade. Insert the rod through the loops at the bottom of the shade. Tie traverse cord to the rod at bottom of each strip of tape. Insert the cord through each ring the length of the shade, at the tops bring all cord across the shade to one side; tie them together and leave 18″ ends. (These cords are drawn to raise the shade.) Insert a curtain rod through the top casing and hang the shade.

ROMAN SHADE

The Roman shade resembles the Austrian shade; however, it is easier to make and requires less time. New cordless tape simplifies the making of a Roman shade. This pleating tape has punched loops instead of rings. Pull tape is laced through the loops and drawn up to pleat the shade.

110

CUTTING THE FABRIC. Measure the window and determine the length and width of the area to cover. To the measured length add 6″ for the top and bottom casing, plus 4″ for each pleat desired. To the measured width add 2″ for side hems and seams. Cut the fabric for the shade by these measurements. Cut the lining 2″ shorter and 2″ narrower than the shade fabric.

JOINING FABRIC AND LINING. Place the lining over the shade, right sides together — with the bottom edges even and the lining 2″ below the top edge of the shade fabric. Pin together along the sides; then stitch making a ½″ seam. Press, then press the seam open.

FINISHING THE BOTTOM EDGE. The bottom edge may be shaped or straight. Pin fabric and lining together across the bottom edge with the fabric extending ½″ beyond the seamline on each side. Mark the design (scallops were used) on the wrong side of the lining. Stitch following the design. (If a straight edge is used, make a ½″ seam.) Press. Trim both edges to within ¼″ of the stitching. Cut notches in the seam edges and slash at the point of the scallops.

Turn the shade to the right side. Fold the scallops on the stitching line and press. Along each side fold the shade fabric ½″ from the seamline and press.

TOP AND BOTTOM CASINGS. At the top edge, pin the lining to the fabric. (Lining is 2″ below top of shade fabric.) Turn the edge of the fabric under ½″ and press. Then turn 1″ to the wrong side, overlapping the lining edge ½″. Pin, then stitch in place from one side edge to the other; backstitch at each end. Press.

Lay the shade with the lining side up. Turn the bottom edge up 6″ from the finished edge; pin near fold about 1½″ from the fold, marking the stitching line. Stitch along the marking; backstitch at each end.

ATTACHING THE PLEATING TAPE. A strip of tape is always placed near each side edge. Additional strips are placed 10″ to 15″ apart. When the bottom edge is scalloped, the tapes should be placed in line with the points of the scallops. Cut the strips of tape the length of the distance between the bottom of the top casing and the top of the bottom casing plus 1″ for turning. Begin each tape with the first loop in the same position so that the folds will lie smoothly. See A.

Lay the shade on a flat surface, wrong side up. Measure 1″ to 4″ from each side edge and lightly mark the vertical line for the tape with chalk. Pin a strip of tape over the marking and between the top and bottom casings. Turn the ends of the tape under 2″ and pin. Stitch in place along each side of the tape and across the ends. Stitch a strip of pleating tape at the opposite side.

Now divide the distance between the outside tapes into two or three equal sections, depending on the number of strips, tape you plan to use. Measure and mark the lines for the tape. Stitch a strip of tape over each marking. Be sure the punched loops of the strips of tape match horizontally.

Cut strips of pull tape 6″ longer than the strips of pleating tape. Turn the end under ½″ and sew it in place at the bottom end of the pleating tape. Thread the tape through the loops every 4″ or 5″, depending on the amount allowed in your measurements for the folds. See B.

BOTTOM ROD. Cut the rod 1″ shorter than the width of the shade. Insert it through the bottom casing. The rod adds the necessary weight for the shade to hang smoothly and will retain the shape at the bottom.

ATTACHING THE ROLLER. Select the roller and attach the pull-tape to it with any adhesive-backed tape. Lay the shade on a flat surface. Then roll the roller toward the bottom of the shade and draw the pull-tape to pleat the entire shade. Be sure the pleats are smooth and even. See C.

HANGING THE SHADE. Insert an adjustable curtain rod through the top casing on the shade. Secure the brackets for the roller and for the curtain rod. Hang.

111

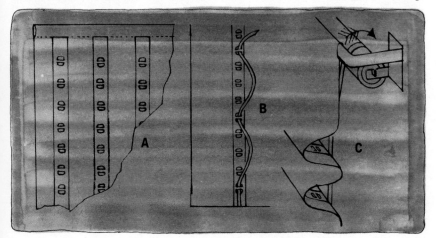

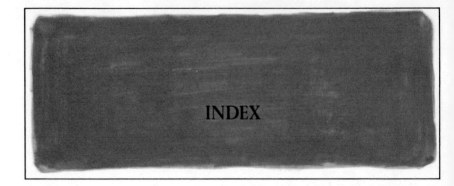

INDEX

113

SUPER TURBO

PROTECTS THE WORLD

By Lee Kirby

Illustrated by George O'Connor

LITTLE SIMON

New York London Toronto Sydney New Delhi

This book is a work of fiction. Any references to historical events, real people, or real places are used fictitiously. Other names, characters, places, and events are products of the author's imagination, and any resemblance to actual events or places or persons, living or dead, is entirely coincidental.

LITTLE SIMON

An imprint of Simon & Schuster Children's Publishing Division • 1230 Avenue of the Americas, New York, New York 10020 • First Little Simon paperback edition October 2017. Copyright © 2017 by Simon & Schuster, Inc. All rights reserved, including the right of reproduction in whole or in part in any form. LITTLE SIMON is a registered trademark of Simon & Schuster, Inc., and associated colophon is a trademark of Simon & Schuster, Inc. For information about special discounts for bulk purchases, please contact Simon & Schuster Special Sales at 1-866-506-1949 or business@simonandschuster.com. The Simon & Schuster Speakers Bureau can bring authors to your live event. For more information or to book an event contact the Simon & Schuster Speakers Bureau at 1-866-248-3049 or visit our website at www.simonspeakers.com. Designed by Jay Colvin. The text of this book was set in Little Simon Gazette.

Manufactured in the United States of America 0917 MTN 10 9 8 7 6 5 4 3 2 1

Cataloging-in-Publication Data for this title is available from the Library of Congress.

ISBN 978-1-4814-9994-1 (hc)

ISBN 978-1-4814-9993-4 (pbk)

ISBN 978-1-4814-9995-8 (eBook)

CONTENTS

1

IS IT HOT IN HERE?

BEHOLD! SUNNYVIEW ELEMENTARY SCHOOL! INSIDE THESE WALLS, UH . . .

Wait, where are we? Are we even inside the walls of Sunnyview Elementary School?

Turbo the hamster, official pet of Classroom C, lay on his belly. Sweat dripped from his furry forehead. Heat beat down from above, and even seemed to be rising from the ground itself. Around him, all Turbo could see was yellow sand.

Turbo squinted in the bright light. Wavy images seemed to appear from thin air. He saw a . . . slice of pizza? And a . . . monster truck? And a . . . giant dragon? Suddenly, there was a voice.

Turbo blinked. Could it be? Was it really who he thought it was? "Leo?"

Leo helped Turbo up from the rock he had been lying on. "Are you okay?" Leo asked. "You sat down and . . . I don't know . . . spaced out."

"Yeah," said Turbo, wiping his forehead with a paw. "It's really hot here."

Turbo looked around. Now he remembered! He had been visiting his friend Leo in Classroom A. But while Turbo's home in Classroom C was a cozy cage filled with cedar chips and a water bottle, Leo's was a desert-like terrarium.

Leo was an official classroom pet. But like Turbo, Leo was not *just* a classroom pet. Turbo and Leo were both secretly superheroes!

But more on that later.

"Maybe we should get you a drink," said Leo.

Leo took Turbo to a small pool of water that looked like it had been carved out of rock. After a few gulps, Turbo felt much more like himself again.

"You have a really nice place, Leo," he said. "But I'm not sure it's quite right for me."

"I'll say." Leo laughed. "You fuzzy guys can't take the heat!"

Suddenly Leo leaped to his feet. "Did you hear that?"

TAP! TAP! TAP!

"It's the Superpet Superhero League alarm!" exclaimed Turbo. "And three taps means there's a super emergency!"

Wait, what's that you say? You've never heard of the Superpet Superhero League?! Why, the Superpet Superhero League is only the best team of superpets in Sunnyview Elementary history!

Turbo and Leo quickly sprang into action. Within moments, they had transformed into . . .

FISH OUT OF WATER!

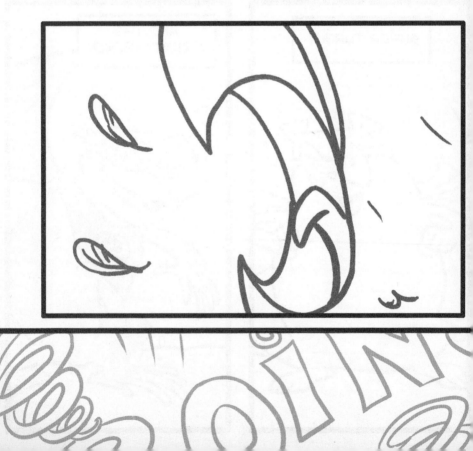

Super Turbo and the Great Gecko
popped the cover off the vent in
Classroom A. The vent system
connected all the classrooms in
Sunnyview Elementary.

The superpets listened closely to
the sound of the taps.

Every member of the Superpet Superhero League used a different tool to tap for help. Turbo, for example, used a ruler. Since this pet was tapping with a pencil, that meant it was Clever!

Clever was a green parakeet, and she was the official pet of Classroom D. She was also a member of the Superpet Superhero League, where

she fought evil as the Green Winger.

Super Turbo followed the Great Gecko down the vent system leading to Classroom D. As they rounded a corner, they bumped into the other members of the Superpet Superhero League.

FRANK

ALIAS: BOSS BUNNY
CLASSROOM: PRINCIPAL'S OFFICE. YEAH, IT'S NOT REALLY A CLASSROOM. FRANK IS THE PERSONAL PET OF PRINCIPAL BAXTER BRICKFORD!
SUPERHERO SKILLS: HIS UTILITY BELT HAS A GADGET FOR ANY OCCASION! AND HE CAN SMELL DANGER!

WARREN

ALIAS: PROFESSOR TURTLE
CLASSROOM: THE SCIENCE LAB
SUPERHERO SKILLS: BEING A TURTLE, HE'S PRETTY SLOW, BUT HE'S ALSO SUPER SMART. ESPECIALLY WHEN IT COMES TO SCIENCE!

The Superpet Superhero League burst out of the vent that led into Classroom D. And there was the Green Winger, perched in her cage. As expected, she was frantic.

"Guys! Thank goodness you're here! Come quick!" she cried. She flew down to the floor of Classroom D and gestured for the other animals to follow her.

As Turbo scurried
along, he nearly
slipped in
something
slick.

"Why is
the floor
all wet?"
he asked.

"*That's* why!" the Green Winger said, and pointed at something flapping on the ground.

It was Nell!

Nell lay on her side. Next to her was an almost-totally-empty Turbomobile.

"Hi, guys," Nell gasped. "A little help here?"

The Turbomobile had once been an ordinary hamster ball until the Superpet Superhero League had turned it into a way for Fantastic Fish to get around. It had allowed the fish to fight in many memorable battles with evil. But now it had apparently sprung a leak.

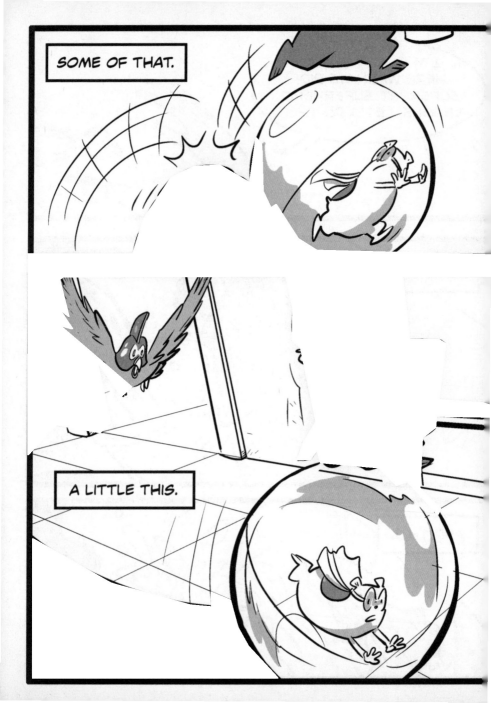

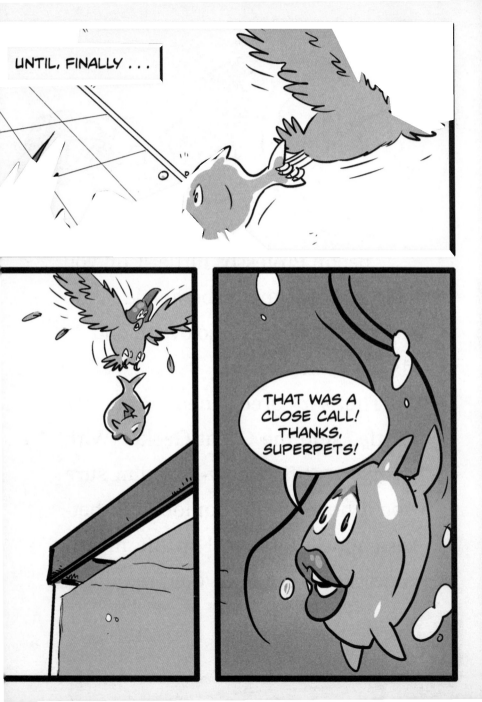

"Wonder Pig . . . ,"
began Professor Turtle. "Can you
help me take the Turbomobile . . . to
my lab? I want to . . . go over it and . . .
fix any leaks."

"That's a great idea, Professor
Turtle," said the Great Gecko. "With
your scientific know-how, I'm sure
you'll have the Turbomobile in better shape than ever! In the mean-
time, tomorrow is our regularly

scheduled Superpet Superhero League meeting. Let's all get some well-earned rest before then."

"It *has* been a long night!" agreed Super Turbo.

And he meant it. As he headed back to Classroom C, he could barely keep his eyes open. Once he was in his cage, Turbo tucked away his superhero gear and fell fast asleep.

THE SUPERPET SUPERHERO LEAGUE GOES GLOBAL!

Turbo woke up early the next morning. He had slept deeply after his adventure in the desert—or, well, in Leo's terrarium—and after his hard work helping Nell.

RING-A-DING-DING!

The classroom bell! That meant school was starting. Since the students of Classroom C had no idea that their beloved class pet was actually a superhero, it was time for Turbo to act like a normal *non*-super hamster. The second-grade students and their teacher filed in.

Turbo ran a few laps on his wheel.

He ate a few hamster pellets.

He drank from his water bottle.

That should do it, thought Turbo, wiping his mouth with the back of his paw. Secret's still safe!

Ms. Beasley, the teacher, began to address the class. Turbo settled into his favorite listening spot next to his food dish. He used to pay no attention to what the teacher told the students of Classroom C, but Turbo had recently discovered that if he *did*

pay attention, he might actually learn something. As in: *learn* about *something* that might require a superhero to step in and save the day.

"Kids, I have exciting news," said Ms. Beasley. "For the next couple of weeks, the whole school is going to be participating in a very special project!"

Turbo's ears perked up. A special project sounded like superhero business.

"And that special project is . . .
Celebrate the World Day!" Ms.
Beasley announced.

"What's Celebrate the World
Day?" asked a student.

"Good question, Sally," replied
Ms. Beasley. "Leading up to the
event, each class at Sunnyview Elementary will research and study
one country. Then, the day of, the
classes will celebrate the country
they've studied! We'll decorate our
classrooms, dress in traditional
clothing, and serve traditional food.
We'll travel around the world by

going from class to class, and we'll learn all about different countries!"

Wow, thought Turbo. *That sounds pretty cool! Maybe we superpets don't need to step in after all.*

Ms. Beasley proceeded to announce which country each classroom would be celebrating.

Turbo listened excitedly. Wow! The whole Superpet Superhero league was involved. But something was missing. There was one pet left out. Turbo couldn't think of who it was. But then . . .

Hey, that's us! How exciting! thought Turbo. *But . . . where's Japan?*

Oh well, he'd have a lot of time to learn. Turbo couldn't wait until the pets' team meeting tonight so they could gush over this exciting new project. The Superpet Superhero League was going global!

Meanwhile, through a small crack in the wall near Classroom C's book nook, a pair of beady eyes were gleaming.

CELEBRATE THE WORLD DAY? MORE LIKE TAKE OVER THE WORLD DAY!

FUN FACTS AND RAT PACKS

That night, all the animals were holding their Superpet Superhero League meeting in the hallway of Sunnyview Elementary. This way, Nell could attend. Professor Turtle was still working on fixing the Turbomobile.

On the way to the meeting, Turbo

and Angelina had stopped by the library to pick up some books, and the animals were eagerly reading up on their classrooms' countries.

The upcoming Celebrate the World Day was very exciting. So exciting, in fact, that the superpets had pretty much forgotten to be super. Instead they just traded cool facts about their countries with one another.

SWITZERLAND . . . HAS THE WORLD'S LARGEST . . . PARTICLE PHYSICS LABORATORY!
BIG DEAL! RUSSIA IS THE BIGGEST COUNTRY IN THE WHOLE WORLD!

The superpets were so wrapped up in all these cool new facts that they didn't notice a couple of small fuzzy animals watching them from around the corner. The two animals whispered to each other and disappeared through a hole in the wall.

If the superpets *had* been paying
attention, they might have seen these
fuzzy creatures, followed them, and
discovered that they went skittering
through the walls, down the halls,
and into the cafeteria, where they
then joined a huge crowd of other
fuzzy creatures. It was . . .

THE RAT PACK!

And in the middle of the pack, standing on a stale bagel, was . . .

WHISKERFACE!

Whiskerface was a tiny rat with huge ears who was just about as evil as they come.

"I need a report on our plans for sabotage!" he bellowed. "Starting with Classroom A!"

Two rats stepped forward. "The kindergarteners of Classroom A will be celebrating Brazil," said one of them. "The most popular sport in Brazil is soccer."

"*Futbol*," corrected the other rat. "They call it *futbol*."

"Yeah, yeah. They're building a miniature *futbol* stadium. We're going to chew through the supports of their tiny stands, and smash it all with a soccer ball attack!"

"Excellent!" said Whiskerface, rubbing his little paws together. "Classroom B! Report!"

Two more rats came forward. "The first-grade students of Classroom B are making their own Leaning Tower of Pisa," said one rat. "We're going to make sure the leaning tower leans over a liiiiiittle too far!"

"Then it will fall, smashing the classroom as flat

as a pizza!" said the other.

Whiskerface laughed his squeaky high-pitched laugh. "Classroom C!"

"The highest point in Japan is Mount Fuji. It's a volcano! The students are making a model," said a rat.

"We're going to make that volcano erupt!" cried his companion nastily.

"Yes! Yes!" shouted Whiskerface, clapping. "Classroom D!"

"Classroom D is Kenya!" another rat announced. "The Third graders are making giant models of safari animals. We will sneak our agents *into* the giraffe model. Bet those kids didn't think a cardboard giraffe could actually walk!"

Whiskerface cackled with delight. "What else do we have?"

"The science lab is going to be Switzerland. They are recreating Lake Geneva. And we're going to make sure that lake overflows!"

"The principal's office will be Russia. They're going to be making borscht." The rat who spoke shuddered with disgust. "Borscht is a cold beet soup. And it's gross. So we kind of figure that's already ruined," he said.

"And, finally," said one rat, as he walked forward, "the hallways are China. In ancient times, China was connected to the rest of the world by trade routes called the Silk Road. The students are turning the hallways into a modern Silk Road."

"But!" said another rat, smiling. "We're going to block the hallways with our very own Great Wall of China! Everyone will be trapped in their classrooms!"

NIGHTTIME NOISES

Turbo was snug as a bug in his
hamster cage when he heard it.
He wasn't sure what it was, but he
knew it was *something*. The last
time Turbo woke up to a strange
sound in the middle of the night, he
ended up having to battle the evil
Pencil Pointer.

He listened as hard as he could with his little hamster ears. He thought he could make out the sound of . . . squeaking?

"Hello? Is anyone there?" Turbo called out.

The squeaking stopped. Well, that was suspicious.

SURELY THIS IS A JOB FOR . . . SUPER TURBO!

Using his super-
hamster agility, Super
Turbo snuck out of
his cage and quietly
scampered across
the classroom to
Ms. Beasley's desk.
That's where the
squeaking seemed to
be coming from.

Super Turbo discovered that the
bottom desk drawer was wide open.
Then he looked up and saw that
the other desk drawers had been
opened, too, but only partway.

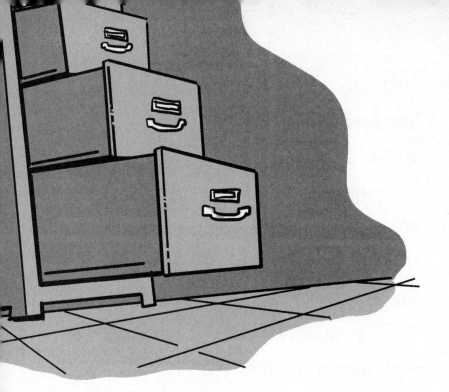

Looks oddly like a staircase, Super Turbo thought. *And what would Super Turbo do? He'd climb that staircase!*

The only problem was . . . even *Super* Turbo was still pretty small.

He took a running start and . . .
SMACK! He bounced off the bottom
drawer.

That was all the boost he needed.
Super Turbo climbed up the drawer-
stairs to the top of Ms. Beasley's
desk and was face-to-face with . . .
no one.

Whoever had opened the drawers, whoever had been here, whoever had been *squeaking*, had left.

From where he now stood on top of Ms. Beasley's desk, Super Turbo realized that he had a perfect view of the whole class and all its decorations!

THE WOOD AND
PAPER SHOJI WALLS
BY THE CUBBIES

THE JAPANESE
GARDEN OVER BY
THE WINDOWS

Super Turbo admired all the hard work the kids of Classroom C had put into Celebrate the World Day. More than ever, he felt that he needed to keep a watchful eye over the classroom.

Suddenly, he heard another noise. But this time, it was different.

The Superpet Superhero Alarm! But which superpet was tapping?

Super Turbo concentrated. The taps were sort of hard and sort of waxy? It was a crayon! That meant he needed to get to Classroom A immediately! The Great Gecko was in trouble!

6

AROUND THE WORLD IN TWENTY MINUTES

All of the superpets had gathered in Classroom A, except for Fantastic Fish, who was still stuck in her tank.

"Just putting a few touches on the Turbomobile," explained Professor Turtle.

The animals were huddled around the Great Gecko, who was staring at a giant piece of paper that lay on the floor. It was slightly torn and a little crumpled.

"Just look at it!" he said sadly. "It's ruined!'

"I'll say!" said Boss Bunny. "It looks like it was painted by a bunch of five-year-olds."

"That's because it *was* painted by a bunch of five-year-olds!" cried the Great Gecko. "This was the banner my kids made to celebrate their country, Brazil! They worked so hard on it. And now it's destroyed!"

"Uh, guys," said Wonder Pig. "If Whiskerface and his Rat Pack are still out there. And we're all in here—"

"Then who's protecting our classrooms?!" cried the Green Winger.

"I think . . . it will be faster . . . if we split up . . . and each go to . . . our own rooms," said Professor Turtle, as quickly as he possibly could. He looked around. The other superpets had already run off. "Oh . . . never mind, then."

The superpets raced through the vents and arrived at Classroom B, Wonder Pig's home.

"Oh no!" Wonder Pig shouted. "The Leaning Tower of

Pisa looks like it's leaning a liiiittle too much!"

Boss Bunny sniffed the air. "I think they've already left! Let's go to the next class!"

The superpets ran to Classroom D, home base of the Green Winger. Just as they arrived, a loud CRASH rang out.

"Oh no!" exclaimed the Green Winger. "They just spilled these beads all over the floor! My kids had been sorting these for days!"

The superpets ran back to the vent and hurried to the science lab. They arrived seconds after Professor Turtle, who had gone straight there at his usual turtle speed. Everything was covered in what looked like snow!

Boss Bunny sniffed the air. "It smells so clean!" he cried with delight.

"That's because . . . these are flakes of . . . *soap*," concluded Professor Turtle. "It's a . . . soapy avalanche!" he said, looking around in horror.

Once again, the superpets were already racing out the door.

"Superpets!" shouted Nell from her aquarium in the hallway. "I just saw them! They ran under the door to the principal's office! If you hurry, you can catch them!"

That did it for Boss Bunny.

No one messed with Principal Brickford's office!

With a mighty bunny hop, Boss Bunny hurled himself at the mail slot in the door of the principal's office.

And the superpets did hurry, but by the time they got the door open, the Rat Pack was long gone.

Fortunately, it looked like they hadn't done any damage there.

But they sure had done a lot to the rest of the school. And it was up to the superpets to fix this mess before the students and teachers arrived the next morning.

It was going to be a long, long night.

7

TODAY'S THE DAY!

It had taken the superpets all night and even into the early morning to clean up the ugly worldwide mess. Then they had spent the rest of the week looking for the Rat Pack in the cafeteria, but Whiskerface and his evil minions were nowhere to be found.

Turbo was in his cage in Classroom C, pacing back and forth. Today was the big one. Today was Celebrate the World Day. If the Rat Pack was going to pull some dirty move, it was going to happen *now*.

Turbo was sure that they were planning something *truly* evil.

Suddenly Turbo noticed that one of his students was staring at him. Pacing back and forth wasn't exactly normal hamster behavior, so he

quickly ran over to his hamster wheel and began running on it.

To be fair, Turbo wasn't looking very *normal* right now anyway.

As part of Celebrate the World Day, some students had dressed Turbo in a hamster-sized traditional Japanese outfit. Turbo thought it looked pretty cool, though it didn't really leave room for his cape.

Turbo glanced at the clock. Soon, the students of Classroom C, along with the rest of Sunnyview Elementary, would head to the school cafeteria. That was where they were having the great feast with food from around the world.

The Superpet Superhero League had decided that as soon as all the kids left their classrooms, the pets would gather for an emergency meeting.

It was risky business. They had never met during school hours before, but they had never faced such a threat before either! Whatever Whiskerface and his Rat Pack were up to, they had to be stopped!

And the Superpet Superhero League was the school's only defense.

RING-A-DING-DING!

The lunch bell rang, and the students of Classroom C filed out of the classroom. Turbo slipped from his cage, crawled down the table, and made his way to the vent. He managed to awkwardly tuck his cape into his kimono.

He scurried through the vents to the meeting place: below the aquarium in the hallway. When Super Turbo arrived, he gasped.

Suddenly, a squeaky voice rang out behind the superpets. "Well, I think you look like a bunch of ninnies!"

It was Whiskerface! And his Rat Pack!

PROTECTING THE SCHOOL—AND THE WORLD!

Whiskerface paced back and forth, gleefully rubbing his paws together. "Do you know why today is a great day? Not only am I going to defeat the superpests—I'm going to ruin Celebrate the World Day, and then I'm going to take over the *actual* world!" he cackled.

"We're *not* going to let you ruin Celebrate the World Day!" cried Turbo.

"Oh really?" said Whiskerface with a sneer. "Well, guess what? You're too late!"

Whiskerface snapped his fingers. On cue, the Rat Pack swarmed the hallway. They linked arms to form a rather disgusting-looking chain of rats, completely blocking the hall.

The Rat Pack advanced on the superpets. On the other side of the wall, Turbo saw that a second group of rats was creating a tower by standing on top of one another so that they could lock the cafeteria door. If they reached that lock, they really *would* trap the entire school!

"We've got to stop them!" cried Turbo. But how?!

Suddenly, a loud rumbling sound filled the hallway.

"I *still* say you left a few steps out of that plan of yours!" yelled Fantastic Fish. She was in the new-and-improved Turbomobile. And riding on top was Boss Bunny!

THE FANTASTICALLY FISHY PLAN!

The Fantastic Fish Tank burst through the great wall of rats, scattering them like bowling pins. Boss Bunny hopped off the back, joining his friends.

"Sorry we're late," he apologized.

"Actually, I'd say you guys were right on time!" cried Super Turbo.

Meanwhile, Fantastic Fish spun down the hallway in her Fantastic Fish Tank. She smacked into the tower of rats.

"What are you doing?!" screamed Whiskerface to his Rat Pack. All the rats were walking around a bit dazed. "Get that talking fish!" he shrieked.

But Fantastic Fish was a few steps ahead of the evil rat. She steered the Fantastic Fish Tank at full speed right for her aquarium.

The Superpet Superhero League stared at her, afraid of what was about to happen.

At the last second, Fantastic Fish unlatched the top of the Fantastic Fish Tank. Then she leaped out. And just in the nick time!

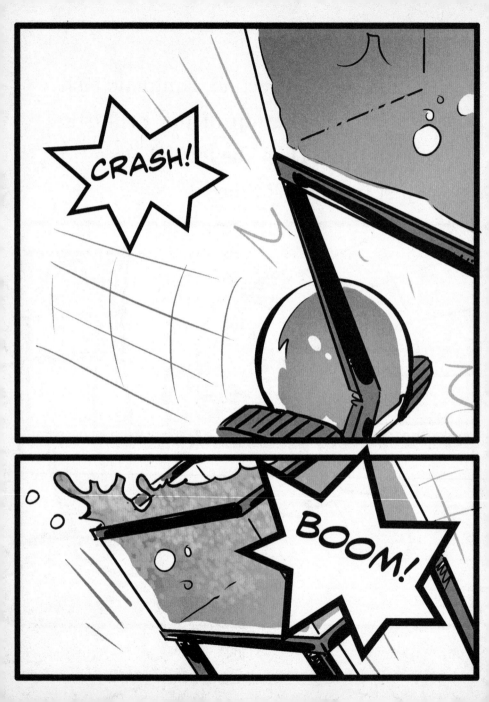

Whiskerface and the Rat Packers were soaked. If there's anything rats hate more than loud noises and superpets, it's being wet. Crying like babies, Whiskerface and his Rat Pack scampered down the hallway.

The superpets ran over to Fantastic Fish, who lay flopping in a shallow puddle.

"Oh no!" cried the Green Winger. "Not again!"

"Get back to your classrooms," gasped Fantastic Fish. "Turbo, hide the new Fantastic Fish Tank. Oh, I also renamed the Turbomobile. Is that okay?"

"Of course it is!" said Super Turbo. "But we can't leave you here!"

"Listen, I'll be fine," Fantastic Fish said. "With the commotion we created, people are going to come running. Any second now, someone will help me."

"Now, that's what I call a hero!" said the Great Gecko.

"Guys . . . we've got . . . to go. I hear someone . . . coming," said Professor Turtle.

The rest of the superpets heard it too. With a last glance at Fantastic Fish, Super Turbo and the others raced away just as Ms. Beasley and a crowd of students burst from the cafeteria.

10

SAFE AND SOUND

A little while later, Turbo sat in his comfy cage, munching on some seaweed and edamame. What a day it had been! The Superpet Superhero League had faced perhaps their greatest challenge yet, and they had won! And to top it off, they had even kept their secret identities safe.

Turbo turned to look at the glass jar next to him on the shelf.

"Care for some edamame?" he asked Nell.

After the commotion in the hallway, Ms. Beasley had been the first to find Nell. She'd taken Nell back to Classroom C and put her safely

inside a jar of water, just until her aquarium could be replaced.

"No, thanks," Nell replied. "I'm more of a dried worm kind of gal."

The students of Classroom C were busy presenting all they knew about Japan to students from other classes.

They would never know how close Celebrate the World Day had come to being ruined, but that didn't matter. Turbo was just glad that Whiskerface had been stopped . . . this time. Surely there would be another time

when the school—and the world—
needed protecting. And when that
time came . . .

THE SUPERPET SUPERHERO LEAGUE
WOULD BE THERE!

MI-TEE!

Visit
CaptainAwesomeBooks.com
for completely awesome
activities, excerpts,
tips from Turbo, and
the series trailer!